STUART SMITH

A View
the Iron

with a Foreword by
SIR HUGH CASSON

and an Introduction by
BARRIE TRINDER

published by
The Ironbridge Gorge Museum Trust

Detail of engraving by Fittler after Robertson, published in 1788 (cat no 29).

Designed and produced for The Ironbridge Gorge
Museum Trust by Thames and Hudson Ltd, London.

Filmset by Keyspools Ltd, Golborne, Lancashire.

Printed and bound in Great Britain by
Balding & Mansell, Wisbech, Cambs.

FOREWORD

This book has been produced to coincide with the exhibition, 'A View from the Iron Bridge', held in 1979 at the Royal Academy. We are delighted to be associated with one of the principal events in an extensive national programme organised by the Ironbridge Gorge Museum Trust to commemorate the bicentenary of the building in 1779 of the first iron bridge in the world, over the River Severn at Coalbrookdale. This event represented the climax to a century of industrial activity and innovation in and around this Shropshire river gorge foreshadowing the unprecedented industrial explosion that spread like wildfire during the nineteenth century and was to transform the look of the world.

Artists and writers from the beginning sensed what was happening, perhaps without fully comprehending the true nature of the genie that had been let loose in Coalbrookdale. This book and the related exhibition demonstrate the astonishing wealth of visual material which documents, sometimes calmly and at other times with a sense of terror, the Iron Bridge and the increasingly industrialised landscape around it. As industry spread throughout Britain, so Coalbrookdale became progressively less important. Furnaces closed and ironworks were deserted. The bridge itself, however, remains as one of England's most spectacular sights.

In 1968 the Ironbridge Gorge Museum Trust was set up. Since then, numerous sites and buildings have been restored, and many converted to museum use, making one of the most remarkable museum complexes in the world. In 1977 I had the pleasure of serving as Chairman to a Committee which gave to Ironbridge the British Museum of the Year Award, a decision later to be enthusiastically confirmed when, the following year, a European Committee gave it the even more prestigious European Award. Though Ironbridge has enjoyed much support from the Telford Development Corporation (which is responsible for setting up the New Town of Telford and which is bringing much needed industry to what was a declining area), the museum, like the Royal Academy, is an independent organisation. It relies on public support and on its own enthusiastic efforts to gain commercial and other valuable forms of sponsorship. If the 1979 exhibition does nothing else but encourage Londoners and others who come to the R.A. to go to Ironbridge, then it will indeed have been worthwhile. I can assure them that they will not be disappointed.

We are grateful to Neil Cossons, the Director of the Ironbridge Gorge Museum, and his colleagues, for enthusiastically persuading us to put on an exhibition at the R.A. Finally, may I add how much we hope that it will stimulate research towards a large-scale exhibition that surely should take place soon, designed to chart and celebrate the response of artists to the Industrial Revolution throughout Britain, Europe and indeed, the rest of the world. That would be a fascinating project which the 1979 exhibition about Coalbrookdale and its Iron Bridge would most appropriately herald.

HUGH CASSON
President of the Royal Academy of Arts

7.iii.79.

INTRODUCTION
by Barrie Trinder

'The largest ironworks in England', ran the response to a question included in a cate-chism of general knowledge published in the 1820s, 'are carried on in Colebrook Dale in Shropshire, a scene as distinguished for its romantic scenery as for its valuable productions'.[1] The spectacular setting of the foundries, furnaces and forges of the Severn Gorge attracted a multitude of artists in the late eighteenth and early nineteenth centuries. More than fifty are known to have depicted the area between 1750 and 1830, among them painters as important as J. M. W. Turner, J. S. Cotman and Joseph Farington. Many of their works were engraved and published, and helped to shape people's general awareness of industry. To some extent artists followed in the wake of ironmakers, engineers and industrial spies, who flocked to Shropshire to learn about the many innovations in the making and use of iron which had taken place there:[2] the smelting of iron with coke instead of charcoal, various methods of manufacturing wrought-iron, the first iron rails and railway wheels, the ingenious system of tub-boat canals, and the casting of such items as cannon, steam-engine cylinders and large bellied pots. Some artists were attracted by spectacular scenery: flaming furnaces framed by the steep cliffs of the Gorge, the dark depths of the Coalport Tar Tunnel, which reminded classically educated visitors of Hades, the smoke-shrouded limekilns of Lincoln Hill, viewed from such a height that the men and horses who laboured about them appeared as mere playthings. Some artists visited the Severn Gorge for no better reason than that it lay on the route from London to the mountains of North Wales. But it is likely that above all what brought artists as well as other visitors to the district was the Iron Bridge, and the bridge is the most consistent and most memorable image in the whole corpus of representations of the Gorge.

The Iron Bridge over the River Severn near Coalbrookdale was universally acknowledged in the late eighteenth century as the first in the world.[3] It was erected between November 1777 and January 1781 under the terms of an Act of Parliament passed in 1776. The idea of building a bridge in iron had first been propounded in 1773 by Thomas Farnolls Pritchard, a Shrewsbury architect, who had long-standing connections with the ironmasters of the Shropshire coalfield. The scheme was energetically supported by John Wilkinson, the most celebrated ironmaster of the time, and carried into effect by Abraham Darby, the third man of that name to direct the Coalbrookdale ironworks. Darby was treasurer to the project, directed every detail of the construction of the bridge, and may well have suffered considerable financial losses through his involvement with it. The design underwent many changes between the time the bridge was first proposed and its completion, but the rings and ogees between the ribs, which are entirely decorative, suggest that the final design was Pritchard's, since the same motif appears in a gazebo at a house in Ludlow which he rebuilt. He died in December 1777 when construction had scarcely commenced. The stone abutments were erected during 1778. The most spectacular phase of construction, the lifting into place of the ribs, took place during the summer of 1779, and the bridge was opened to traffic on New Year's Day 1781.

The image of the Iron Bridge was vigorously promoted by its proprietors. It was a toll bridge, and while most of its revenue was derived from local sources, strenuous efforts were made to persuade long-distance travellers to use it. Some six months before the bridge was completed, in June 1780, the secretary to the proprietors advertised in the press that 'a view of the cast iron bridge engraved by a capital artist' was soon to be published.[4] This was probably the view by Michael Angelo Rooker, scene painter at the Haymarket Theatre, to whom Abraham Darby paid £29 as fee and expenses in travelling from London to paint the bridge. In October 1780 Darby paid ten guineas to William Williams 'for drawing a view of the bridge'.[5] By May 1781 Rooker's drawing, engraved by William Ellis, was on sale, together with 'an elevation of the bridge with its principal parts', which was given free to subscribers. A subsequent edition, published in 1782 by the Coalbrookdale Company, was dedicated to King George III.[6] These views were deliberately and consciously promoted by the builders of the bridge, who were obviously aware of the symbolic properties of the structure they had created.

The qualities of the bridge were speedily recognised by coach promoters and hotel proprietors. An advertisement for the Swan Inn proclaimed that it was 'situate near that most incomparable piece of architecture, the Iron Bridge'.[7] The route from Shrewsbury to Bridgnorth over the bridge was claimed 'to afford as many agreeable prospects as any road of the same extent in the kingdom'. A Shrewsbury to London stage coach was advertised as passing 'that striking specimen of Art and so much admired object of travellers'.[8] The landlord of one hotel in 1802 recommended his facilities to 'families that wish to stop and see the Manufactories in Coalbrookdale'.[9] For about thirty years the ironworks of the Severn Gorge, and their associated mines and transport systems, were places to be visited, in the same way that the limestone caves of Derbyshire, the rapids and abbeys of the Wye Valley, or the mountains of North Wales were visited. The accounts of many travellers described the main sights on the tourists' itinerary through the Gorge: the Coalbrookdale ironworks, the limestone workings on Lincoln Hill, the Tar Tunnel, the boring mills at the Calcutts ironworks, the 'big wheel' at the Benthall corn mill, and the china works at Coalport. The one sight which no visitor missed was the Iron Bridge itself, and it is not surprising that it dominates the records of the Gorge left by artists as well as those of writers. 'As there are many plans & drawings of the Iron Bridge extant', wrote one visitor in 1799, 'it is needless for me to describe it'.[10]

The Severn Gorge was not unknown to artists even before the construction of the Iron Bridge. Thomas Robins made a series of sketches in the area in the 1750s, and in 1758 two engravings of Coalbrookdale by François Vivares were published 'for those who are curious in the works of Nature or of Art'. William Williams painted two pictures of Coalbrookdale in 1777, which were subsequently engraved, although no copies of the engravings are known to survive. The paintings reflect feelings very similar to those of Arthur Young, expressed on a visit to Coalbrookdale the previous year:[11]

> Colebrook Dale itself is a very romantic spot . . . a winding glen between two immense hills which break into various forms, and all thickly covered with wood, forming the most beautiful sheets of hanging wood . . . too beautiful to be much in unison with that variety of horrors art has spread at the bottom.

Williams shows the pools of the ironworks surrounded by smoke- and flame-topped furnaces, and fuming piles of coal being coked and ore in the process of calcination. The steam pumping engine, topped by a huge column of smoke, is accorded a prominent place in both views. In the 'Afternoon View of Coalbrookdale', the ironworks appears cut off from the surrounding countryside by the woods on the valley slopes. The people in the corner of the picture, a red-coated gentleman talking to a rustic, and two elegant, gossiping females, appear largely unconcerned with the spectacle below them. William Williams's view of the Iron Bridge, painted about three years after the Coalbrookdale picture, shows very different attitudes. The bridge is the centre of all attention, notably from a gentleman in a punt-like vessel in mid-stream, who is enthusiastically showing off the bridge to two seated ladies. Similarly, spectators examining the bridge from below, from the banks and from the river, can be seen in many of the other published views of the bridge. Michael Angelo Rooker drew the bridge from a similar position to that chosen by Williams. He shows two gentlemen closely and seriously examining the ribs of the bridge, while from a distance it is surveyed by a man in a broad-brimmed hat, a well-dressed lady and a dog. Travellers in carriages, on horseback and on foot are seen crossing the bridge, while a poacher with his dog stalks along the north bank. A barge is anchored on the south bank near which a pitcherwoman was gathering river water. Through the arch smoke pours from the chimneys of what is probably a lead-smelter, while a coracle bobs on the current below the bridge. Above the arch there towers a rocky crag, but it is mere background scenery, altogether secondary to the man-made bridge spanning the river. Rooker was clearly aware of the many human activities carried on along the banks of the Severn, but it is the bridge, the achievement of those who lived in the Gorge as well as the property of his patrons which dominates both the natural landscape and the human figures within it. The bridge is similarly the dominant feature of many other views of the Gorge. The three pictures by George Robertson painted in 1788 show it overshadowed by the surrounding hills, but quietly, even in the distant view from the bottom of Lincoln Hill, it commands the whole landscape. Pictures provide valuable evidence of the replacement of the high stone abutments on the south bank of the Iron Bridge with timber land arches, a matter on which the evidence from the proprietors' minutes is confusing. Paul Sandby Munn on 11 July 1802 sketched the land arches under construction and W. Smith in 1810 depicted them in a finished state. The timber arches had a short life and were replaced by the present cast-iron arches in the early 1820s.

The views by Rooker and Robertson perhaps more than any others popularised the bridge, and made its image a familiar one among the educated classes. It became even more widely known as it appeared on pottery, on bill-headings, on trade tokens and around the ash-holes of cottage grates. It was a copy of the Rooker print that was bought for thirteen shillings by Thomas Jefferson when he was in London in 1786, and later hung in the presidential residence in Washington.[12] The bridge became so well-known in Europe that the next two iron bridges known to have been constructed were both small-scale replicas of it, one in a park at Raincy near Paris, and the other at Worlitz near Magdeburg in Prussia.[13] Several publications printed in German in the 1780s and 1790s described the bridge, while its visitors included Swedish industrial spies, an American paper maker, the Prince and Princess of Orange, a count from Venice and Princess Carbristka of Poland.[14]

A lithograph of the Penrhyn Slate Quarries by W. Crane of Chester, 1842.

The Carclase tin mine, from an etching by
Samuel Middiman after Joseph Farington, 1813.

Detail of engraving published in 1782 (cat no 18).

Once drawn to the Gorge by the bridge, artists delighted in the wildness of its furnace fires, the steepness of its surrounding hills and the crude, groaning, wooden mechanisms of its pitheads and waggonways. The paintings of the area by Paul Sandby Munn, J. M. W. Turner and J. S. Cotman accord well with the feelings of sublime horror expressed by many writers of the 1790s and the first decade of the nineteenth century when visiting industrial enterprises in dramatic natural surroundings. They were fascinated, and at the same time they were struck with a degree of terror. Henry Skrine wrote of Parys Mountain in 1798, that it was,

> by far the greatest curiosity Anglesey can boast, and its most considerable source of wealth. ... as a spectacle it is not a little striking to behold a large arid mountain entirely stripped of its herbage by the steam of the sulphur works, and perforated with numberless caverns which, opening under lofty arches one below the other, seem to disclose the deepest arcana of the earth.[15]

Richard Ayton said of the harbour of Portreath in the Cornish mining district in 1813 that,

> in all its parts, in spite of the efforts of art, [it] still preserves an appearance so savage and unhewn, that it furnishes a most satisfactory specimen of the wildest of the wilds of Cornwall. A few chimneys and a little smoke give it a slight air of improvement, but nature has cast it in so uncouth a mould, that it can never be altogether turned or chiselled and planed into forms of comfort and regularity.[16]

The workers in industrial enterprises were often regarded by writers or painters with paternalistic condescension, or even lofty disdain. The Revd Richard Warner said of Neath Abbey in 1798 that,

> The ruins are of prodigious extent, but being in the immediate neighbourhood of the metal works and inhabited by the squalid families of the workmen employed there, they do not produce the pleasing emotions that religious remains, under different circumstances, so naturally and generally do inspire.[17]

A more usual reaction was that of Arthur Young who, on visiting the Severn Gorge in 1776, remarked on the cheerfulness and plenty which he found among the 'humble but happy inhabitants of this romantic spot'.[18] It was still possible in the late eighteenth century to see industry as William Bray saw the Derby silk mill in 1777, as something which worked 'to the great relief and comfort of the poor',[19] and uninhibitedly to welcome the opportunities for employment which it brought.

This was an attitude which was no longer possible after the French wars of the early nineteenth century. The optimistic view of industrial progress which characterised the years that followed the construction of the Iron Bridge was never again wholly tenable. Furnaces, cotton mills or copper mines could no longer be regarded as curious phenomena, which happily created employment for the poor. The effects of pollution were becoming all too apparent, particularly when unrelieved by spectacular scenery. J. G. Kohl remarked on passing from Birmingham to Stafford in 1842 that he was 'delighted to have a clear view of the sky again'.[20] As early as 1814 Richard Ayton described Amlwch, the town nearest to Parys Mountain, as a place from which families were fleeing, where houses were falling down, but where still, owing to the decline of copper mining there were more people than could find work:

A plate from *The Costumes of Yorkshire*:
'Factory Children', aquatinted by Robert Havell
after George Walker.

'Love Conquered Fear', an engraving for *The
Life and Adventures of Michael Armstrong*, 1840.

> This wretched town stands in the midst of a hideous scene of desolation; the country round looks as if it had been blasted by a horrid pestilence and raises in the mind no images but of misery and famine.[21]

In industrial Shropshire the closure of a succession of ironworks in the years after 1815 brought great poverty, and caused the flight of numerous colliers and furnacemen to other districts. By the 1830s many hand-loom weavers in textile districts had similarly lost all hope of consistent employment. It was no longer possible to be wholly optimistic about technological progress once the cyclical nature of the industrial economy had become apparent, and once it was appreciated that the adoption of innovations created human casualties. It was increasingly realised that industry was not simply a means of creating prosperity for society as a whole. The wealth that it brought was not evenly distributed. While manufacturers, and to a greater extent land owners prospered on profits, rents and royalties, and skilled and trusted workers might in the short term be well paid and tolerably housed, their prosperity depended on the ill-rewarded labour of the unskilled, and on the casting aside of those whose skills were rendered redundant by injury, old age or innovation. Political repression during and immediately after the wars with France further emphasised the deep divisions within British society. By the 1830s the urban problems, usually but sometimes wrongly associated with industrialisation, were becoming overwhelming. The 'Condition of England' debate around 1840 was to a large extent a debate about urban squalor, which was regarded with the same horrified fascination with which spectacular ironworks or copper mines had been regarded half a century earlier. Léon Faucher said of Manchester in 1844 that it was 'the most extraordinary settlement, the most interesting, and in some ways the most monstrous that social progress has yet produced'.[22] The foreigner interested in social and economic change visiting England in the 1840s was likely to inspect the cheap lodging houses of Liverpool or Manchester, when fifty years earlier he would have taken delight in the Iron Bridge or Arkwright's mills at Cromford. When factories were discovered which did not cause pollution, and where employees were not shamelessly exploited, they were discussed defensively, as exceptions to an assumed rule that the effects of industry were harmful.

The heroic tradition of industrial art continued into the nineteenth century but it was increasingly isolated from the mainstream of social thought, and from developments in the art world as a whole. John Cooke Bourne, in recording for posterity the building of the London and Birmingham and Great Western Railways, was clearly fired with admiration for the breathtaking scale of the enterprises, but this sense of wonder was tempered for the public by what was known of the disruption caused in cities by railway building.[23] The growth of the railway system and the spread of sizeable industrial enterprises to many market towns made industrial scenes less of a novelty than they had been in the late eighteenth century. When addressing the Lakeland mountains in 1844, William Wordsworth wrote,

> Now for your shame, a Power, the Thirst of Gold,
> That rules o'er Britain like a baneful star,
> Wills that your peace, your beauty, shall be sold,
> And clear way made for her triumphal car
> Through the beloved retreats your arms enfold!
> Heard YE that Whistle? As her long-linked Train
> Swept onwards, did the vision cross your view?[24]

The lack of attention given by artists to the horrors of the great cities in the 1840s, when they were such a universal topic of concern, is impressive. Many turned away from the disorders of the time to seek solace in the piety of the Middle Ages. After 1830 no artist of more than parochial repute depicted the Iron Bridge until the revival of interest in the monuments of the Industrial Revolution began in the 1950s. The Gorge was seen by polite society as J. E. Auden described it in 1912: 'an uninteresting and somewhat squalid town, situated on a steep declivity sloping down to the Severn whose banks are here covered with slag and refuse'.[25]

The Iron Bridge was built at a propitious moment in English history, when industrial development could be seen as bringing unalloyed benefits to the poor, and at the same time exalting the achievements of Englishmen over other nations, and of Man over natural forces. It was still possible in the 1780s and 1790s to hold wholly sanguine expectations about technological change and economic growth. The art of that period reflects both these views, and the sense of horror mixed with excitement and admiration felt by artists viewing the ironworks of the Severn Gorge. But the paintings are a part of social history as well as the history of art. They are part of the historical process, not merely comments upon it. They record the scenes in and around Coalbrookdale at the time when Britain was in process of becoming the first industrial nation, undergoing a painful experience which has become almost an universal one. It was a time when landless labourers from the remotest parts of the Borderland were seeking to find employment in and around the ironworks and mines, when some ironmasters were becoming wealthy and some were applying to industrial processes the findings of science, a time when religious revivals of epic scale were breaking out. The pictures record not just the artists' admiration for the ingenuity of the Shropshire ironmasters, nor merely their enthusiasm for the nearest equivalent that could be found in England to erupting volcanoes. They preserve a record of the scenery against which the Industrial Revolution and the making of the English working class were enacted.

Notes to the Introduction

1. David Blair, *The Mother's Question Book*, 1834, 169.
2. For a full account of the economic and social history of the district see Barrie Trinder, *The Industrial Revolution in Shropshire*, 1973.
3. The construction of the bridge is fully described in N. Cossons and B. Trinder, *The Iron Bridge: symbol of the Industrial Revolution*, 1979.
4. *Shrewsbury Chronicle* (henceforth *SC*), 10 June 1780.
5. Abraham Darby's Cashbook 1769–1781, 64/66, Shropshire Record Office 1987/19. Abraham Darby's Ledger Accounts, 55, Shropshire Record Office 2448/1.
6. See Catalogue nos 16–18.
7. *SC*, 17 July 1781.
8. *SC*, 25 March 1786.
9. *SC*, 14 May 1802.
10. Simon Goodrich, quoted in B. Trinder, '*The Most Extraordinary District in the World*', 1977, 60.
11. Arthur Young, *Tours in England and Wales*, 1932 ed, 152.
12. William Howard Adams, ed, *The Eye of Thomas Jefferson*, National Gallery of Art, Washington, DC, 1977, 62.
13. N. Cossons and B. Trinder, *op cit*, 67.
14. B. Trinder, '*The Most Extraordinary District in the World*', 1977, 36, 47, 48, 72.
15. Henry Skrine, *Two Successive tours through the whole of Wales with several of the English counties*, 1798, 627.
16. Richard Ayton, *A Voyage round Great Britain undertaken in the summer of 1813*, 1814, I, 119.
17. Richard Warner, *A second walk through Wales in August and September 1798*, 1813 ed, 95–6.
18. Arthur Young, *op cit*, 145.
19. William Bray, *A Tour through some of the Midland Counties to Derbyshire and Yorkshire in 1777*, 1783 ed, 371.
20. J. G. Kohl, *Ireland, Scotland and England*, 1844, 10.
21. R. Ayton, *op cit*, II, 12.
22. Léon Faucher, *Etudes sur l'Angleterre*, 1845, I, 315.
23. Francis Klingender, *Art and the Industrial Revolution*, 1972 ed, 134.
24. William Wordsworth, *Shorter Poems*, Everyman ed 1907, 664–5.
25. J. E. Auden, *Shropshire*, 1912, 138.

Abbreviations used in the Catalogue

Acc	accession
ARA	Associate of the Royal Academy
b	born
bc	bottom centre
blc	bottom left corner
BL	British Library (Reference Division)
BM	British Museum
brc	bottom right corner
B. Trinder, *Extraordinary District*	Barrie Trinder, '*The Most Extraordinary District in the World*', Phillimore 1977
B. Trinder, *The Industrial Revolution*	Barrie Trinder, *The Industrial Revolution in Shropshire*, Phillimore 1973
Col	collection
d	died
Ex	exhibited at
FSA	Fellow of the Society of Antiquaries
Klingender 1947/1968	Francis D. Klingender, *Art and the Industrial Revolution*, 1947 and 1968 (revised and enlarged edition)
Lit	literature
Manchester 1968	Manchester City Art Gallery 1968: *Art and the Industrial Revolution*
RA	Royal Academy; Royal Academician
repr	reproduced
tc	top centre
tlc	top left corner
trc	top right corner
V & A	Victoria and Albert Museum, London

NOTE: Unless otherwise stated, the works listed are without signature or other inscription. All dimensions (height before width) quoted refer to the size of the image.

1a

1. THOMAS ROBINS (1715–70)
Views on the River Severn
Pen, wash and pencil, 10 × 18 in (254 × 458 mm).

A sketchbook, containing 133 drawings by Thomas Robins, has at least seven views of the River Severn in the Coalbrookdale area, executed in the 1750s. Only one of them (f, below) has a title.

1b

a) inscribed brc 'No. 82' (a large house with grounds coming down to the River, on which are four trows). Possibly depicts Dale End, Coalbrookdale, with Lincoln Hill.

b) inscribed brc 'No. 83', and 'JULY 29' at tlc. (a house on the right of the river bank with a ferry carrying two men on horseback and many boats). Possibly Quatford.

c) inscribed tlc 'Gd. N' (a view across the river with a high hill over which winds a steep road). Possibly Benthall Edge, Coalbrookdale.

d) inscribed brc 'No. 86' (the river with two trows and an inclined plane descending the hill on the opposite bank where there are houses and waggons). Possibly Benthall Edge or Lincoln Hill.

e) inscribed brc 'No. 87' and, on the river in the foreground, 'Severn' (the river, with two houses between which is a gated road leading to the water). Possibly the south bank of the River Severn where the Iron Bridge now stands.

f) inscribed, in top margin, 'Near Coalbrookdale in Shropshire.', brc 'No. 116' (a view of the river from Blists Hill with the Calcutts on the left bank and Broseley in the distance).

g) not inscribed (same view as f; the hill in the background is The Wrekin).

Lit: John Cornforth, 'In pursuit of Thomas Robins', *Country Life*, 25 Dec. 1975.
Col: Royal Institute of British Architects (Private Collection).

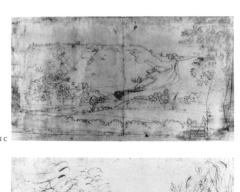

1c

1d

1e

1g

1f

These drawings, discovered only in 1972, come from a sketchbook which depicts many houses and gardens up and down the country. Robins was born at Charlton Kings near Cheltenham in 1715, and possibly moved to Bath in 1740. His earliest drawing is of the King and Queen's Bath, which is dated 1747, and his latest, 1765. He died in 1770.

Thomas Robins had a son, also called Thomas, who was born in 1745 and became a flower

2

painter. He, like his father, was forgotten after his death, but in 1967 he was rediscovered when some of his pictures were sold. Almost all the paintings attributed to the elder Robins are based on drawings in this sketchbook and whilst many of them are of places quite close to Bath, it is clear that he made tours as well. On his first Shropshire tour in 1753, he sketched Davenport Hall and on his second tour he carried out the seven sketches here mentioned. It is not certain whether they predate the two illustrations by François Vivares but in style they are certainly much earlier.

2–4 FRANÇOIS VIVARES (1709–80) after THOMAS SMITH (d 1767) and GEORGE PERRY (1719–71)
2. *The Upper Works at Coalbrookdale*
Engraving, hand coloured, $15\frac{3}{8} \times 21\frac{1}{2}$ in (390×546 mm).
Inscribed, lower margin, brc 'F. Vivares Sculpt.'; centre 'A VIEW of the Upper Works at Coalbrook Dale, in the County of /SALOP./ Designed and Published by G. Perry and T. Smith 1758, according to Act of Parliament.'; blc 'No. 1'.
Col: Elton Collection, Ironbridge Gorge Museum Trust.

Lit: Klingender 1947, pp. 74–5, 169 pl II; A. Raistrick, *Dynasty of Ironfounders*, 1953, p 72; Klingender 1968, pp 87, 203, No 2, repr pl II.
Ex: Manchester 1968 (273).

These engravings of Coalbrookdale, the earliest known of this subject, were published in 1758, a year after Burke's treatise *On the Sublime and the Picturesque*.
The Coke Hearth in Coalbrookdale takes its name from the location shown in this engraving. Coking is taking place in the foreground adjacent to the Furnace Pool. A team of horses are pulling a cylinder for a steam engine along Wellington Road and the smoke from the Coalbrookdale Furnace can be seen in the middle foreground. Darby Road rises to the right.
George Perry, who lived in Coalbrookdale and was the principal partner in the Lightmoor Ironworks, was co-publisher of these engravings and also wrote a prospectus for the two engravings (see item 4). (See Barrie Trinder, *The Most Extraordinary District in the World*, Phillimore 1977, p. 88.) Perry executed in 1772 *A Plan of the Iron Works at Madeley Wood in Shropshire* (BL, Map Library, King's Topography 36/16/1).
Thomas Smith of Derby, the other co-

3

5

publisher of these engravings, earned the reputation of being one of the first English painters of landscape, particularly in the Peak District, the Yorkshire Dales and the Bristol Avon. He was the father of the celebrated engraver John Raphael Smith (1732–1812).

3. *South West Prospect of Coalbrookdale*
Engraving, hand coloured, $15\frac{3}{8} \times 21\frac{7}{16}$ in (390 × 545 mm).
Inscribed, lower margin, brc 'F. Vivares, fecit'; centre 'The South West Prospect of Coalbrook-Dale, and the Adjacent Country. / Designed and Published according to Act of Parliament by Geo. Perry and T. Smith, 1758.'; blc 'No. II.'
Col: Elton Collection, Ironbridge Gorge Museum Trust.
Lit: See item 2, *Upper Works at Coalbrookdale*.
Ex: Manchester 1968 (274).
This engraving was also published as a book plate; there are slight differences, especially in the horses in the foreground.
Engraving, $4\frac{1}{8} \times 7\frac{3}{8}$ in (104 × 188 mm).

Inscribed, lower margin centre, 'A View of Coalbrook-Dale in Shropshire and the adjacent Country.', from *England Displayed*, 1798, inscribed, tlc 'VII' and trc 'p. 233'; also from the *Gentleman's Magazine*, inscribed, tlc 'VII' and trc 'p. 221'.

Of particular interest in this engraving is the team of pack horses probably carrying coal or iron ore down to the furnaces through the well-wooded Dale. The various houses shown on the engraving include Dale House, Rose Hill House and Tea Kettle Row. On the extreme right can be seen Sunnyside and in the centre is a circular tower which is possibly the building shown as a windmill on some early maps.

4. *A Description of Coalbrookdale in the County of Salop with two prospective views thereof*

The subscribers to these engravings included the familiar families of Coalbrookdale and Shropshire together with the first known reference to John Baskerville of Birmingham, the famous printer. (Not illustrated)

6

7

5–7. WILLIAM WILLIAMS (c 1740–1798)
5.   *A Morning View of Coalbrookdale*
Oil on canvas, 40⅜ × 49½ in (1025 × 1256 mm),
signed 'W. W. 1777'.
Col: Burwell Hall, Lincs; Marshall Spink;
purchased from him by the National Art-
Collections Fund and presented to Shrewsbury
Art Gallery, 1954.
Lit: F. D. Klingender, 'Quaker Dynasty', in
The Architectural Review, CXV (March 1954),
pp 157–61, repr p 161; *Fifty-First Annual
Report of the National Art-Collections Fund:
1954–1955*, p 43.
Ex: RA 1778 (344, as *A Morning View of
Colebrook Dale, and part of the extensive iron
works*); Manchester 1968 (69).

This view of Coalbrookdale, taken from the top
of Jiggers Bank, shows a team of horses being
used to brake a loaded coal waggon descending
the hill. In the centre of the picture can be seen a
pumping engine and to the right of the engine
is the smoke of the furnaces. A very similar
view was executed by John Cox Bayliss in
1856; see item 109 and note to item 6.

6.   *An Afternoon View of Coalbrookdale*
Oil on canvas, 40⅜ × 49⅜ in (1024 × 1254 mm),
signed 'W. W. 1777'.
Col: same as no 5.
Ex: RA 1778 (345, as *An afternoon view of
Colebrooke Dale and part of the extensive iron works,
from Lincoln Hill, terminated by the celebrated
mountain Wrekin*); Manchester 1968 (70).
Lit: same as No. 5.

These two paintings were also engraved on
18 × 33 inch plates and on sale in the Autumn of
1777 at 1 guinea a pair, but no examples are
known to survive. The 'Afternoon View',
taken from the top of Lincoln Hill, shows the

Lower Furnace Pool and Upper Forge Pool
with the Lower Furnace in between. The Upper
Furnace cannot be seen but the smoke emitted
from there rises towards Dale Road. This
painting compares well with a plan of Coalbrookdale drawn in 1753, now in the possession of the Ironbridge Gorge Museum
Trust.

7.   *A View on the River Severn*
Pencil drawing, with grey and brown wash,
11¼ × 20¼ in (285 × 515 mm).
Inscribed, top, 'A View on the River Severn at
Madely near Coalbrook Dale and where the
iron bridge is to be built'.
Col: Aberdeen Art Gallery, scrapbook contain-
ing 92 drawings by William Williams and
others, presented by Miss Lizzie Hogarth,
Sherborne, 1957.
Lit: 'A Famous Bridge in Art', *Country Life*, 12
Sept 1957, p 486.

Williams was awarded a premium by the
Society of Arts in 1758 and in the 1760s he is
known to have been painting portraits in
Norwich. He moved to London in 1766 and
from the early 1770s submitted works quite
frequently to the Royal Academy and other
exhibitions. He travelled widely on sketching
tours, as can be gathered from the titles of his
paintings, and around 1776 or 1777 he visited
the Coalbrookdale area. As a topographical
landscape artist Williams had a keen eye for the
new industrial landscape which presented itself
so magnificently in the Severn Gorge. Williams
was probably commissioned to paint the bridge
and first made a pencil and wash drawing of the
proposed site, taken from the north bank
looking upstream. Boats line the bank of the
river and there is also a man paddling a coracle.

8.   Anonymous
Thomas Farnolls Pritchard
Oil on canvas, 28½ × 23½ in (724 × 597 mm).
Col: purchased 1978 from the descendants of
Pritchard by the Ironbridge Gorge Museum
Trust.

This picture, together with a similar portrait of
Mrs Pritchard (both works having remained

8

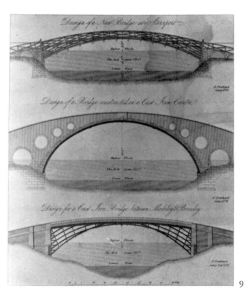

9

continuously in family possession), was probably painted in the early 1770s, as Pritchard
died before the construction of the Iron Bridge.
His role in the design and construction of the
bridge is fully discussed in the Ironbridge
Gorge Museum guide 3·01, *The Iron Bridge*.

9.   JOHN WHITE
*Design for a Cast Iron Bridge between Madeley and
Broseley*
Engraving, 7¾ × 6¼ in (197 × 159 mm) (one of
three engravings on same plate, at bottom).
Inscribed, above bridge, 'Design for a Cast Iron
Bridge between Madeley & Broseley'; brc
'F. Pritchard / Salop Oct. 1775'; in margin, blc
'J. White delt.' and brc 'G. Gladwin Sculpt.'
From *On Cementitious Architecture as applicable to
the Construction of Bridges by John White, Architect,
with a prefatory notice of the first introduction of iron
as the constituent material for arches of large span by
Thomas Farnolls Pritchard in 1773*, London,
printed by Richard Taylor, Red Lion Court,
Fleet Street, 1832, extracted from the *Philo-
sophical Magazine and Annals*, vol XI, p 183.
Col: Ironbridge Gorge Museum Trust.

10.   WILLIAM WILLIAMS (*c.* 1740–1798)
The Cast Iron Bridge near Coalbrookdale
Oil on canvas, 34 × 40 in (863 × 1016 mm),
signed bl 'W. WILLIAMS 1780'.
Col: Sir Alexander Gibb and Partners.
Lit: B. Trinder, *The Industrial Revolution*, p 788.

In October 1780, Abraham Darby III paid
Williams 10 guineas for this charming view of
the Iron Bridge. In a boat there are two ladies in
their fine hats and an equally elegant gentleman
who appears to be pointing out some detail of
the Iron Bridge to them, while a boatman
controls the vessel. In the distance can be seen a
number of trows and the industriousness of
others in the painting emphasises the leisurely
life which the gentry in the boat appear to lead.
This painting was thought lost for over 150
years until it was finally traced to Sir Alexander
Gibb & Partners of Reading in 1974. Note the
great similarity between this and the Rooker
drawing (see item 15).

11, 12.   MODELS OF THE IRON BRIDGE
A large model of the Iron Bridge was by May
1782 in the possession of Sir Edward Smythe of
Acton Burnell who paid a Shrewsbury firm
£2.12s to paint it. Another model of the bridge,
now   in   the   Science   Museum,   South

10

12

Kensington, was built in 1785 by Thomas Gregory; in 1787 Abraham Darby III presented this model to the Society of Arts which, 'Sensible of the magnitude and importance of the Iron Bridge', granted him its gold medal in May of the following year.

11. Royal Scottish Museum Model, 119 in (3025 mm) long, 39½ in (1000 mm) high and 25 in (635 mm) deep (origin of model unknown).
12. Science Museum Model $\frac{1}{24}$th scale, 78½ in (2000 mm) long, 31½ in (800 mm) high and 17¼ in (440 mm) deep (illustrated above).

13

13. J. EDMUNDS
A View of the Iron Bridge
Woodcut, $12\frac{1}{2} \times 18\frac{1}{2}$ in (343×470 mm).
Inscribed, top, 'A View of the Iron BRIDGE, erected over the River SEVERN near COALBROOKE-DALE in the County of SALOP'; and with, bottom, a description of the bridge and 'MADELEY: Printed by J. EDMUNDS.'.
Col: Ironbridge Gorge Museum Trust.

Edmunds was a local printer and this woodcut was probably issued as a broadsheet immediately after the construction of the bridge. A different version exists in which the centre roundel of the bridge encloses the initials 'A.D.'.

14. Attributed to MICHAEL ANGELO ROOKER (1743–1801)
Ironbridge, Coalbrookdale
Pen, sepia and colour wash, $14\frac{1}{2} \times 23\frac{1}{2}$ in (368×600 mm).
Col: Stanhope Shelton Pictures, Suffolk, 1975; City of Coventry Art Department, Acc no 1975/19.

Whilst this picture cannot be ascribed with certainty, it is probable that it is a preliminary study by Rooker (no 15). It differs only in the figures and the amount of traffic passing over the bridge.

15. MICHAEL ANGELO ROOKER, ARA (1743–1801)
The Cast Iron Bridge near Coalbrook Dale
Pen, ink and watercolour, $15\frac{1}{2} \times 24\frac{1}{2}$ in (394×622 mm)

Col: Aberdeen Art Gallery, purchased Webster bequest 1954, Acc no 54.31.
Lit: 'A famous bridge in Art', *Country Life*, 12 Sept 1957, p 486; B. Trinder, *The Industrial Revolution*, p 189, 'In January 1781 Michael Angelo Rooker, scene painter at the Haymarket Theatre, travelled to Coalbrookdale from London to make a drawing of the bridge, his fee and expenses amounting to £29.' This, however, refers to the date of payment; the visit was in early 1780.

Having studied painting under Paul Sandby, Rooker worked for some time as an engraver, working for such publications as *The Virtuosi's Museum* and *The Copper Plate Magazine*. He became a scene painter for the Haymarket Theatre, during which time he was commissioned by Abraham Darby III to paint a picture of the Iron Bridge. This painting was engraved by William Ellis and these engravings were dedicated by the Coalbrookdale Company to George III on 4 July 1782.
The brightly lit scene shows the Iron Bridge in the centre of the composition and through its arch one catches a glimpse of the lead smelter.
Rooker has turned a blind eye to the horrors of the Dale in which Robertson revelled (see no 31). In this respect Rooker differs from his teacher, Paul Sandby, who was described by Gainsborough as 'the only man of genius' who painted 'real' views from nature in this country'. Rooker did not find a very good market for his watercolours which were made on sketching tours around Britain.

14

15

16–18. WILLIAM ELLIS (1747–d before 1810) after MICHAEL ANGELO ROOKER (1743–1801)

16. *View of the Cast Iron Bridge near Coalbrook Dale*
Engraving, $14\frac{3}{4} \times 23\frac{3}{4}$ in (374×603 mm).
Inscribed, bottom centre 'View of the Cast Iron Bridge near *Coalbrook Dale*', and on the stones in middle foreground, 'M. Rooker delin. 1780, Wm Ellis, aqua forte fecit 1781.'
Col: BL, Map Library, King's Topography 36/26g.
Lit: B. Trinder, *The Industrial Revolution*, p 189, 'Views of the bridge by a *capital artist* were on sale in June 1780.'

This very early engraving, possibly a first proof, shows no figures on the bridge and appears unfinished.

17. *The Cast Iron Bridge near Coalbrookdale*
Engraving, hand coloured, $17\frac{1}{2} \times 26\frac{1}{8}$ in (446×661 mm).
Inscribed, lower margin, blc 'Drawn by M. A. Rooker'; brc 'Engraved by Wm. Ellis'; centre 'To George the Third, King of Great Britain etc. / This View of the CAST IRON BRIDGE, near COALBROOKDALE in the County of Salop– / Is by permission most respectfully inscribed, by His faithful and dutiful Subjects – The Coalbrook Dale Company. – LONDON: Published as the Act directs, 4th June 1782, by Jas. Phillips, George Yard, Lombard Street.'
Col: Ironbridge Gorge Museum Trust.
Lit: M. Chappell, *British Engineers*, 1942, repr fp 9 (colour); Klingender 1947, p 75; Klingender 1968, p 88.
Ex: Manchester 1968 (157); Washington DC, *The Eye of Thomas Jefferson*, 1976 (110).

The stones in the foreground show faintly the traces of the wording in item 16. The print originally cost 13s and was available from Mark Gilpin of Coalbrookdale or from London and Shrewsbury booksellers.

18. *The Iron Bridge cast at Coalbrookdale.*
Engraving, 17×22 in (432×559 mm).
Inscribed with, bottom centre, a description of the bridge, and bc 'Published as the Act directs 1782, by James Phillips in George Yard, Lombard Street.'
Col: Ironbridge Gorge Museum Trust.
Lit: as 17.

Subscribers who purchased the engraving by Ellis after Rooker were offered, as a free gift, 'an elevation of the bridge with its principle parts etc. on a sheet the same size as the print', quoted in B. Trinder, *Industrial Revolution*, p 189.

17

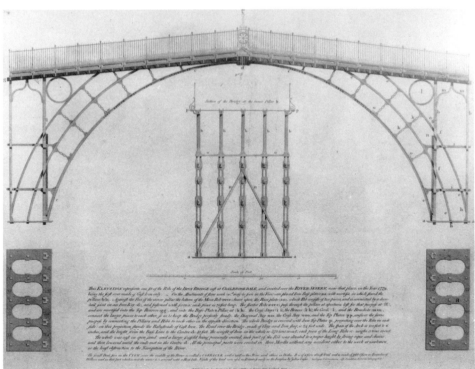

18

Section of the Bridge at the inner Pillar

Scale of Feet

This ELEVATION represents one fit of the Ribs of the IRON BRIDGE cast at COALBROOKDALE, and erected over the RIVER SEVERN, near that place, in the Year 1779, being the first ever made of Cast Iron only — — . On the Abutments of stone work *a a* may be seen at the Fore-side placed Iron Base plates *x x*; with overlaps in which stand the pillars *b b c c*. Against the Feet of the inner pillars the bottom of the Main Ribs meet, shoot upon the Base plates *x x x*, which Rib consists of two pieces, and is connected by a dove-tail joint in an Iron Key *d d*, and fastened with screws, and pins in perfect snug. The footer Ribs *e e e e*; pass through the pillars at apertures left for that purpose at *ff*, and are received into the Top Braces *g g g*, and into the Base Plate at Pillar at *h h*. The Cross-Stays *i i*, the Braces *k k*, the Circle *l l*, and the Brackets *m m m*, connect the larger pieces to each other *p* so to keep the Bridge properly firmly. The Diagonal Stay *n n*, and the Top Plates *p p*; enforce the same purpose by connecting the Pillars and Ribs to each other in the opposite direction. The whole Bridge is erected with two Top Plates *q*, projecting over the Ribs on each side : on this projection stands the Balustrade of Cast Iron. The Road over the Bridge, made of Clay and Iron slag, is 24 feet wide. The span of the Arch is perfect to *s s* inches, and the height from the Base Line to the Centre *t t*, 40 feet. The weight of Iron in the whole is 378 tons 10 cwt. each piece of the Long Ribs *e e* weighs 5 tons 5 cwt.

The whole was cast in open sand : and a larger scaffold being previously erected, each part of the Rib was directed to proper height by being rope and chains and then lowered until the ends met in the Centre *t t*. All the principal parts were erected on River Months without any accident either to the work or workmen, or the least obstruction to the Navigation of the River.

The small Boat seen in the VIEW, near the middle of the River is called a CORRACLE, used in half on the River, and others in India. It is of a form much used and is made of light Oziers or Basketwork Withers and in that part where the water is a general width a Rope slide. Width of the boat over and on Boards and on the keepless by John Taylor.   Antiqua Corporation. &c London delineation drawing &c.

Published by the late Messrs 1780 by Edward Phillips, at George Yard, Lombard Street.

23

19

19. *The Cast Iron Bridge near Coalbrookdale*
Handkerchief, sepia print on linen, 27 × 28¼ in (685 × 717 mm).
Inscribed as 17 and description from 18, at bottom, 'Engraved and Printed by Adams and Lay by Permission of the Proprietors of the Print from which it is copied.'
Col: Ironbridge Gorge Museum Trust.

20. *Fireplaces with Iron Bridge Motif*
Cast-iron, semi-circular fire basket with matching semi-circular ash hole, around which is the Iron Bridge. Flanked by two vertical panels. There are two separate varieties: a) inscribed in scrolls above bridge, 'Plan of the Iron Bridge at Coalbrook Dale', marked 'C Dale'; b) inscribed in scrolls on either side of fire basket, 'A View of the Cast Iron / Bridge over the Severn'. 24 × 38 in (610 × 695 mm).
Col: a) Ironbridge Gorge Museum Trust; b) Private Collection.

21, 22. E. EDGCOMBE
21. *A View of the Cast Iron Bridge*
Lithograph, 16½ × 22¾ in (420 × 580 mm).
Inscribed, bc 'A View of the CAST IRON BRIDGE, over the Severn at COALBROOK DALE in Shropshire, Published May 1st 1782 as the Act directs by R. Bagwell, No. 3, Queen Street, Cheapside'; blc 'E. Edgcombe del.'; brc 'C. West fecit'.
Col: BL, Map Library, King's Topography 36/26d.

22. *A View of the Cast Iron Bridge*
Aquatint, 15 × 18¾ in (381 × 476 mm).
Inscribed, bc 'A View of the CAST IRON BRIDGE over the Severn at COALBROOK DALE in Shropshire, published 1st December 1786 by Robt. Wilkinson No. 58, Cornhill London' brc 'C. West fect.'; blc 'E. Edgcombe delin.'
Col: Morley Tonkin (60), Ironbridge Gorge Museum Trust

These two engravings differ considerably and the one executed in 1782 appears to be more complete than that of 1786. The 1782 engraving shows the date and inscription on the Iron Bridge together with well executed figures whereas the 1786 engraving appears to have ghost figures on both the trow and the Iron Bridge itself. Both engravings are probably taken from the downstream side of the bridge with Benthall Edge shown on the left bank.

21

22

23–5. THOMAS FREDERICK BURNEY (1765–85)
23. *The Iron Bridge, Coalbrookdale*
Watercolour, 7⅝ × 11⅛ in (194 × 290 mm).
Col: Dr Percy 1890, The Dowager Lady Swinton, Thomas Agnew & Sons 1973 (53), Mellon Collection.

Burney was a cousin of the novelist Fanny Burney. He exhibited a portrait of a gentlemen at the RA in 1785. In 1784 he was apprenticed to the engraver Heath. He was a talented topographer and worked with his brother, E. F. Burney. Burney was born in Worcester and died in Shrewsbury. The team of men pulling the trow upstream are bowhaulers. The viewpoint of the artist is from the present Wharfage looking downstream.

24. *The Iron Bridge*
Engraving, 5 × 7½ in (127 × 190 mm).
Inscribed, 'sculp. by W. & W. Walker, pub. April 30th 1784 by R. Baldwin, Paternoster Row.'
'View of the Iron Bridge over the River Severn,

23

25

near Coalbrookdale, Shropshire.' from the *London Magazine*, April 1789, p 312 vol II.
Col: Salop County Library, Watton Newspaper Cuttings, vol 6.

The Library has another version of this engraving which omits the engravers' names and is inscribed 'Published by Alexr. Hogg No. 16 Paternoster Row.'

25.   *View of the Iron Bridge*
Engraving, 5 × 7½ in (127 × 190 mm)
Inscribed, bc 'View of the Iron Bridge over the River Severn, near Coalbrookdale, Shropshire.'; blc 'T. F. Burney del.'; brc 'W & J. Walker sculp'; bc 'Published by Alexr. Hogg, No. 16 Paternoster Row.' (also known without date and name of Hogg).
Col: Ironbridge Gorge Museum Trust; a plate from Newman's *Curiosities of England and Wales*, 1789.
Lit: B. Trinder, *The Industrial Revolution* repr fp 68.

A remarkably exact copy of the original by Burney (item 23).

26.   GEORGE ROBERTSON (1724–88)
The Iron Bridge from Lincoln Hill
Oil on canvas, 24 × 29 in (610 × 737 mm).

Col: The Parker Gallery, purchased by the Ironbridge Gorge Museum Trust 1978.

Robertson painted a set of six views of the Coalbrookdale area which were published as engravings in February 1788 by Josiah Boydell. All but one of the original paintings are now lost, although the engravings made from them are well known.
Robertson was conscious of the great contrast between the romantic beauty of the area and the sublime horrors of the industry within it. These six works were engraved by three engravers – Francis Chesham, James Fittler and Wilson Lowry. Robertson had travelled widely with William Beckford of Somerley. Having visited Italy, they then travelled to Jamaica *c* 1770, and there Robertson painted a number of views, six of which were engraved and published by the Boydells. On returning to England Robertson set up as a drawing master and landscape painter.
John Boydell, the eighteenth-century print seller, was born in 1719 at Dorrington in Shropshire. His father was a land surveyor and estate agent and John was intended for the same profession. Instead he decided to make a career in the world of art, and in 1741 despite parental opposition he walked to London where he became a student at the St Martin's Lane Academy and apprenticed himself to a minor engraver, William Henry Toms. Although he worked hard he did not reach fame as an engraver but instead became known as an entrepreneur. In 1748 he married Elizabeth Lloyd, the second daughter of Edward Lloyd of Oswestry, and by 1752 he had earned enough money from the sale of his landscape engravings to set up his own publishing house. He continued engraving for some 15 years, but was content to function mainly as an employer of other craftsmen. In his career he is said to have employed over 260 engravers and he commissioned many artists. About 1771 he took his nephew, Josiah Boydell, into the firm as an apprentice. During the 1780s he commissioned a series of paintings to illustrate scenes from Shakespeare which were exhibited in the Shakespeare Gallery in Pall Mall. This enterprise was not a financial success and on Boydell's death in 1802 the majority of these paintings, together with his other assets, were auctioned. As a result of this sale these works were dispersed, and it is therefore not surprising that the other five paintings of Coalbrookdale by Robertson can no longer be found.

26

27

27, 28.　Francis Chesham (1749–1806) after
George Robertson (1724–88)
27.　*The Iron Bridge, Coalbrookdale, from Lincoln
Hill*
Engraving, 16 × 22⅜ in (406 × 568 mm).
Inscribed, below image, blc 'G. Robertson,
Pinxit.'; brc 'Francis Chesham, Sculpsit.';

centre 'A VIEW of the IRON BRIDGE, in Coalbrook DALE, SHROPSHIRE. Taken from the
bottom of LINCOLN HILL. Published Feby. 1st
1788, by John & Josiah Boydell, No. 90,
Cheapside London.'
Col: Elton Collection, Ironbridge Gorge
Museum Trust.

28

29

28

30

Lit: C. F. Bell in *The Walpole Society*, V, 1917, pp 54–9, esp p 55; Klingender 1947, pp 67, 75–6, 154; Klingender 1968, pp 89–91.
Ex: Manchester 1968 (132).

The Chesham engraving differs very little from the original oil painting by Robertson and shows Ironbridge before the construction of The Wharfage. On the extreme right of the picture is the lead smelter which was situated below Benthall Edge.

28. *The Mouth of a Coal Pit near Broseley*
Engraving, $16\frac{1}{8} \times 22\frac{3}{8}$ in (408 × 568 mm).
Inscribed, below image, blc 'G. Robertson Pinxit.'; brc 'Francis Chesham. Sculpsit.'; centre 'A VIEW of the MOUTH of a COAL PIT near BROSELEY in SHROPSHIRE. / Published Feby. 1st 1788, by John and Josiah Boydell, No. 90, Cheapside London.'
Col: Elton Collection, Ironbridge Gorge Museum Trust.
Lit: As item 27.
Ex: Manchester 1968 (131).

The engraving shows a coalpit on the edge of a wood, drawn in the romantic style of Rosa, whose works Robertson had studied in his youth. The woodland contrasts dramatically with the huge horse-driven wheel, the toiling

figures and the rough ground around the pit. The engraving shows a ventilating chimney much used in early mines to remove noxious gases from below ground. The horse-gin was used to raise the coal from below and the engraving depicts two forms of transport, viz. plateway waggons and pack animals. The location of the engraving is unsure but a similar gin pit is shown in other illustrations of the area, particularly those by Thomas Hearne and the anonymous sketch (no 98). An old woman is shown tending the pack horses, a practice which is confirmed by documentary sources.

29, 30. JAMES FITTLER (1758–1835) after George Robertson (1724–88)
29. *The Iron Bridge, Coalbrookdale, from the Madeley side*
Engraving, $14\frac{7}{8} \times 21$ in (379 × 533 mm).
Inscribed, below image, blc 'G. Robertson, Pinxit.'; brc 'James Fittler, Sculpsit.'; centre, 'A VIEW of the IRON BRIDGE, taken from the MADELEY side of the River SEVERN, near Coalbrook DALE, in the County of SALOP. / [left centre] This Bridge was erected in 1779. It is the first that / was ever made of Cast Iron only. The abutments are stone / & cover'd with plates of Iron. The Road over the Bridge is / 24 feet wide, the span of the Arch is 100 feet & 6 Inches

and the / [right centre] height from the Base line to the Center is 40 feet, the weight of the Iron employed in the whole Bridge is 378 Tons and a half. / All the principle [sic] parts were erected in the course of three Months, / without the least obstruction to the navigation of the River. / Published Feby 1st 1788, by John & Josiah Boydell No. [9]0, Cheapside London.'
Col: Ironbridge Gorge Museum Trust.
Lit: Klingender 1947, p 182, fig 23; Klingender 1968, p 206, no 26, repr pl 26.
Ex: Manchester 1968 (165).

Here Robertson is unconcerned with producing the kind of purely pictorial account of the bridge that can be seen for instance in Rooker's work. He shows the bridge, placed right of centre in the composition, surrounded by towering slopes of hanging woods. The figures in the foreground are dwarfed into insignificance by the magnificence of the scenery in which they stand. Unlike most pictorial accounts of the bridge which show it in full daylight, here it is shown with only the left abutment in full light. This and the brightness of the craggy peak above it contrast sharply with the dark foreground and the shaded slopes to create a very real sense of the romantic beauty of the area.

30. *Lincoln Hill and the Iron Bridge, Coalbrookdale*

Engraving, hand coloured, $15\frac{7}{8} \times 21\frac{3}{4}$ in (402 × 548 mm).
Inscribed, lower margin, blc 'G. Robertson, Pinxit.'; brc 'James Fittler, Sculpsit.'; centre 'A VIEW OF LINCOLN HILL, with the IRON BRIDGE in the DISTANCE. Taken from the side of the River SEVERN. / Published Feby. 1st 1788, by John & Josiah Boydell, No. 90 Cheapside, London.'
Col: Ironbridge Gorge Museum Trust.
Lit: See No. 29.
Ex: Manchester 1968 (164).

Fittler and Chesham were not outstanding as engravers and worked in various fields. Wilson Lowry on the other hand was a talented scientist as well as an artist, and played an important part in the development of the steel engraving.
This view shows the stacking and loading of coal into Severn trows prior to transport down river. The area shown in the foreground is now known as Dale End. Nailors' Row is clearly visible. It stood on the present car park adjacent to the Severn Warehouse.

31, 32. WILSON LOWRY (1762–1824) after George Robertson (1724–88)
31. *An Iron Work for Casting Cannon*
Engraving, 16 × 22$\frac{3}{8}$ in (407 × 568 mm).
Inscribed, below image, blc 'G. Robertson Pinxit.'; brc 'Lowry, Sculpsit.'; centre 'An IRON WORK, for Casting of CANNON: and a

32

Boreing MILL, Taken from the MADELEY side of the River SEVERN. SHROPSHIRE. / Published Feby. 1st 1788, by John & Josiah Boydell, No. 90, Cheapside London.'
Col: Elton Collection, Ironbridge Gorge Museum Trust.
Lit: Klingender 1947, p 175, fig 12; Klingender 1968, p 205, no 14, repr pl 14; B. Trinder, *The Industrial Revolution*, p 68.
Ex: Manchester 1968 (216).

This view of the Calcutts ironworks, looking downstream from the Bedlam Furnaces, shows a corn mill in the foreground and the blast furnaces and foundry as occupied by Alexander Brodie. The works were constructed about 1770 and were purchased in 1786 by Brodie, a self-made Scotsman, who had worked as a blacksmith in London. He concentrated on the manufacture of cannon and ships' stoves of the type he patented in 1764. Charles Hatchett went to the Calcutts in 1796 and watched thirty-two pounder cannon being cast two at a time, and then bored 7 or 8 at a time in a boring mill powered by a steam engine. In August of the same year the Prince and Princess of Orange included the Calcutts on their tour of Shropshire. They were saluted by the firing of guns and were taken to see the boring of 10 cannons at a time. A Swedish visitor to the works in 1802–3 found 11 horizontal borers worked by the steam engine in the boring mill. A plan of the works about the turn of the

century shows the range of tar ovens built by Lord Dundonald in the late eighteenth century.

32.   *The Inside of a Smelting House at Broseley*
Engraving, 16 × 22¾ in (406 × 568 mm).
Inscribed, below image, blc 'G. Robertson Pinxit.'; brc 'Wilson Lowry, Sculpsit,'; centre 'THE Inside of a SMELTING HOUSE at BROSELEY SHROPSHIRE. / Published Feby. 1st 1788, by John & Josiah Boydell No. 90, Cheapside London'.
Col: Elton Collection, Ironbridge Gorge Museum Trust.
Lit: Klingender 1947, p 175, fig 13; Klingender 1968, p 205, no 15, repr pl 15; A. Raistrick, *Quakers in Science and Industry*, 1950, fp 97.
Ex: Manchester 1968 (215).

To portray the industrial activity in the Dale, Robertson first chose to paint the cannon foundry and boring mill at Broseley owned by Alexander Brodie, and then he depicted the inside of a Smelting House at Broseley, engraved by Wilson Lowry. Here the blast furnace is shown at night, making it even more gloomy than normal. We see a few small figures at work who seem to make the house appear even larger. The contrast between this and the glimpse of the serene moonlit landscape outside is startling and serves to reinforce the 'horror' of the smelting house. It is probable that this view is of the same blast furnaces as in no 31.

33

33. LEMUEL FRANCIS ABBOT (1760–1803)
Portrait of John Wilkinson (detail)
Oil on canvas, 30 × 30 in (762 × 762 mm).
Col: Ironbridge Gorge Museum Trust, purchased 1978.

John Wilkinson (1728–1808) was one of the leading ironmasters of the Industrial Revolution who, at various times in his career, had works at Willey, Snedshill, Hollinswood and New Hadley in Shropshire, at Bradley near Bilston in Staffordshire, and at Bersham and Brymbo in Denbighshire. He had close associations with Matthew Boulton and James Watt of Birmingham, who obtained from him cylinders and other iron parts for steam engines.

34. *The Token Coinage of John Wilkinson*
Wilkinson issued three copper tokens between 1788 and 1795, and one silver coin valued at 3*s* 6*d*, but only a hundred of the latter were produced, and it is doubtful whether it was intended as currency, especially since striking private currency in a precious metal was a much more serious breach of the royal prerogative than issuing private copper coins. The silver coin had Wilkinson's bust on the obverse, and a sailing vessel on the reverse, and was a version of Token II, described below. Wilkinson's copper coins are properly described as follows:—

Token I
Obverse: Bust of an eighteenth century gentleman with flowing hair tied behind.
Legend: JOHN WILKINSON IRON MASTER.
Reverse: The interior of a forge showing a large hammer and a workman holding a piece of metal on an anvil, with 1787 in the exergue.
Edge: WILLEY SNEDSHILL BERSHAM BRADLEY.
Diesinker: Hancock. Manufacturer: Hancock. There are nineteen die variants, some rare but mostly common. They are fine, heavy coins well designed. Tokens of this design were also issued in 1788, 1790, 1792, 1793 and 1795.

Token II (not illustrated)
Obverse: Bust of Wilkinson, similar to Token I.
Reverse: A small brigantine under sail, with 1788 in the exergue.
Edge: WILLEY SNEDSHILL BERSHAM BRADLEY.
Diesinker: Hancock. Manufacturer: Matthew Boulton of Soho, Birmingham.
This coin is thought to celebrate the launching of *The Trial*, the first iron boat, at Willey Wharf, Shropshire, in 1787, although the brigantine on the reverse in no way resembles this vessel.

Token III (not illustrated)
Obverse: Bust of John Wilkinson, shown with two more rows of curls in his hairstyle than in Tokens I and II.
Reverse: A nude figure of Vulcan seated on an anvil and striking a piece of metal on a second anvil, with a hammer in his right hand. The metal is held with a pair of tongs in the left hand. The image was copied from an antique gem engraved in Spence's *Polymetis* (plate X, no 1) with the helmet upon which the god was

34/I

32

working in the original, changed to the bar of iron shown on the token. Part of a vessel is shown in the background on the right.

Legend: HALFPENNY, with 1790 in the exergue.

Edge: WILLEY SNEDSHILL BERSHAM BRADLEY.

Diesinker: Hancock. Manufacturer: Hancock.

Similar tokens were issued in 1791 and 1792.

Wilkinson's issuing of tokens is commemorated in two verses from a contemporary popular song:

> *So Wilkinson, from this example*
> *Gives himself a matchless sample*
> *Which shows his modesty and sense*
> *And how and where, he made his pence.*
>
> *Then let each jolly fellow take hold of his glass*
> *And drink to the health of his friend and his lass;*
> *May we always have plenty of stingo and pence,*
> *And Wilkinson's fame blaze a thousand years hence.*

35–7. JOSEPH FARINGTON, RA (1747–1821)
35. *The Iron Bridge near Coalbrookdale*
Pencil, 15⅛ × 23½ in (384 × 597 mm).
Inscribed, brc 'The Iron Bridge near / Coalbrooke Dale and / Country Surrounding.';

bottom right 'Sept. 25 – 1789'. Annotated, left to right: 'Bentley furnace; Green; Lloyds; Bedlam Furnace; Stratton Hill; Lincoln Hill.'
Col: Ironbridge Gorge Museum Trust.
Lit: A. Raistrick, *Dynasty of Ironfounders*, 1953 and 1970, repr fp 112.
Ex: Manchester 1968 (160).

This sketch, done from a very similar viewpoint as that by Robins (item 1f), shows the houses clustered around the riverside at Jackfield and the Calcutts and the beginnings of the settlement of Ironbridge, although more buildings are seen to be adjacent to Bedlam Furnaces. By this date there appeared to be a large number of buildings around the bottom of Lincoln Hill in the area now known as Hodge Bower. On the extreme left of the picture are a group of buildings and a kiln which are probably the Jackfield Potworks which produced the familiar black-glazed earthenware.

36. *Coalbrookdale*
Pencil, 17⅞ × 23⅛ in (454 × 588 mm) inscribed, brc 'Coalbroke [*sic*] Dale. / Septr. 26 – 1789 / 4 pools in all'; left 'The Dale Copy', ie The Dale Coppice.
Col: Ironbridge Gorge Museum Trust.

Lit: A. Raistrick, *Dynasty of Ironfounders*, 1953 and 1970, repr fp 108.

Ex: Manchester 1968 (161).

Farington was known mainly as a topographical draughtsman. He was made a member of the RA in 1785 and his detailed diaries, kept in the eighteenth and early nineteenth centuries, are an important source of information about art and the Royal Academy of that period. Alas, they begin after his visit to Coalbrookdale.

These meticulous pencil studies give a very clear view of how the Dale appeared in the late

eighteenth century. Coalbrookdale is seen here from the Rotunda on Lincoln Hill looking up the Dale. In the left foreground is Upper Forge with its dwellings, malthouse and miscellaneous industrial buildings with the dam wall of the Upper Forge Pool immediately above. In the centre of the picture is the Lower Furnace with its characteristic break-iron which remained until the late nineteenth century. To the right of the Lower Furnace is the John Fletcher Chapel and Charity Row. The Upper Furnace and Darby Road can be seen in the far distance with Jiggers Bank winding its way over the hill to Wellington.

37. *Coalport Bridge*
Pencil sketch, 6½ × 18¼ in (165 × 464 mm).
Inscribed, 'Bridge on the Severn below the Iron
Bridge.'; dated 'Sept 24. 1789'.
Lit: B. Trinder, *The Industrial Revolution*, pl 17.
Col: Morley Tonkin (46), Ironbridge Gorge
Museum Trust.

This sketch is of very great significance as it
shows the bridge at Coalport prior to the
damage caused by a flood in 1795, when it
was replaced by a bridge of single span with
cast-iron arches. See B. Trinder, *Industrial
Archaeology Review*, vol 3, no 2, 1979.

38. THOMAS ROWLANDSON (1756–1827)
*Meadow Wharf, Coalbrookdale, late eighteenth
century*
Watercolour(?), no details known.
Col: Not known.
Lit: A. Raistrick, *Dynasty of Ironfounders*, 1953,
repr fp 96; John Hayes, *Rowlandson, Water
colours and drawings*, Phaidon 1972; B. Trinder,
The Industrial Revolution, p 190.

Unfortunately the whereabouts of this picture
is not known even though it was reproduced by
Raistrick in 1953. It is probable that Rowlandson executed this work in about 1797 when he
is known to have toured North Wales and
when he also carried out other topographical
works of this nature.
The view of the sketch is a little uncertain but it
is probably looking upstream from a point on
the present Wharfage with Benthall Edge on
the left-hand side and the familiar lead smelter.
In the centre foreground is the flat area at
present occupied by the Severn Warehouse. In
the foreground of the picture two peasants are
reclining on a stack of pig iron and to their right
can be seen a motley array of castings awaiting
shipment. Most of these castings appear to be
cooking pots although others must be either
water pipes or cannon. On the extreme right of

the picture a horse is pulling a plateway
waggon on which one pot is standing. The
rugged houses to the right of the picture were
probably swept away during the construction
of the present Wharfage and Market Square.

39. WILSON
Portrait of William Reynolds
Oil on canvas, 37 × 55 in (940 × 1395 mm).
Col: Ironbridge Gorge Museum Trust.

This threequarter-length portrait of William
Reynolds (1758–1803) shows Reynolds holding

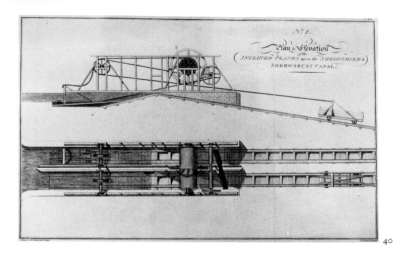

40

41

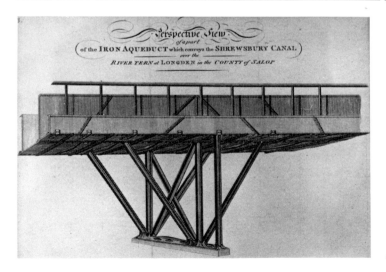

42

43

plans inscribed 'Sketch of the first iron aqueduct cast at Ketley 1795'. It was painted about 1795 by one Wilson of Birmingham who was commissioned to paint the leading iron-masters of the time. The cast-iron aqueduct which is mentioned is situated at Longdon-on-Tern and was designed by Thomas Telford in 1795. It was the first cast-iron canal aqueduct.

40–3.   J. PLYMLEY
Four engravings from Joseph Plymley, *A General View of the Agriculture of Shropshire* (1803), relate to the works of William Reynolds.

40.   *Inclined Planes on the Shropshire and Shrewsbury Canal*
Engraving, $7\frac{3}{4} \times 11\frac{3}{4}$ in (197 × 298 mm).
Inscribed, trc 'p. 294'; title, top right 'No. 1 / Plan & Elevation / of the / INCLINED PLANES upon the SHROPSHIRE & / SHREWSBURY CANAL.'; blc 'drawn for Mr. Telford by W. Jones'; brc 'S. I. Neele sc. Strand'.
Col: Ironbridge Gorge Museum Trust.

A drawing of one of the inclined planes on the Shropshire tub-boat canal, indicating the way in which the boats were transferred from one level to another. From the engraving it appears that U-shaped rails were used and that a hemp rope was used for haulage. The next plate indicates a more sophisticated version of this incline.

41.   *Inclined Planes on the Shropshire and Shrewsbury Canal*
Engraving, $7\frac{3}{4} \times 13\frac{1}{2}$ in (197 × 343 mm).
Inscribed, trc 'No 2 / Plan & Elevation / of the Inclined Planes / upon the / SHROPSHIRE & SHREWSBURY CANAL / with the application of the / FIRE ENGINE.'
Col: Ironbridge Gorge Museum Trust.

The small engine used here drew boats out of the water and also hauled tub boats up the incline whenever there was an imbalance in load.

42.   *Iron Aqueduct at Longden*
Engraving, $6\frac{1}{4} \times 9$ in. (159 × 229 mm).
Inscribed, tc 'Perspective View / of a part / of the Iron Aqueduct which conveys the Shrewsbury Canal / over the / River Tern at Longden in the County of Salop'; tlc '3'.
Col: Ironbridge Gorge Museum Trust.

43.   *Buildwas Bridge*
Engraving $7\frac{1}{2} \times 14\frac{1}{4}$ in (190 × 362 mm).
Inscribed, tc 'Plan Elevation & Section / of the / IRON BRIDGE built on the RIVER SEVERN / at BUILDWAS in the COUNTY of SALOP / in the years 1795 & 1796.'; blc 'Thomas Telford architect'; brc 'S. I. Neele, sculp. Strand'; tlc 'No. 4.'
Col: Ironbridge Gorge Museum Trust.

A fine engraving of the bridge built on a revolutionary new principle by Thomas Telford. Also shown in item 88.

44. *Coalbrookdale Token*

Obverse: View of an iron bridge over a river with a trow passing beneath, inscribed, above the bridge, 'ERECTED ANNO 1779 SPAN 100 FEET'. Legend: 'IRON BRIDGE AT COALBROOK-DALE – 1792'.

Reverse: View of an inclined plane with a man lowering a laden barge by the machinery. 'INCLINED PLANE AT KETLEY. 1789' in the exergue.

Edge: 'PAYABLE AT COALBROOK-DALE AND KETLEY'.

Diesinker: Wyon. Manufacturer: Kempson.

The tokens were struck after the death of the third Abraham Darby in 1789, at a time when the affairs of the Coalbrookdale Company were largely controlled by the Quaker Richard Reynolds and his son William. It is curious that the tokens mention two of the company's ironworks, at Ketley and Coalbrookdale, but not those at Madeley Wood and Horsehay.

The tokens display two of the sights which drew people from all over the world to the Coalbrookdale Coalfield in the late eighteenth century, at which time it was the most important iron-making area in Britain.

The Iron Bridge was built between 1777 and 1781. The iron ribs were put into place in the summer of 1779, which is the year generally quoted as the date of erection of the bridge. Its construction was due largely to the third Abraham Darby, and the Reynolds family had little connection with the project until after its completion.

The inclined plane represented on the reverse was on the private Ketley Canal built by William Reynolds in 1788, to carry coal and iron ore from mines in the Oakengates area to the ironworks in the valley of the Ketley Brook. It was the first inclined plane to be successfully put to work on a canal in Britain. It differed in several respects from five other inclined planes subsequently built on canals in east Shropshire, which had reverse slopes at the top, going down into the water, instead of locks on the main slope, as at Ketley. The Ketley incline was the steepest of those in the area, and had a vertical rise of 66 ft. It was used until about 1816, when the Ketley Ironworks passed out of the hands of the Reynolds family. The site is marked by a road called 'The Incline' adjacent to Ketley Hall. The picture on the token is also shown in the portrait of William Reynolds (see no 39).

44

45. *William Reynolds' Sketchbook*

Sketchbook with 128 engravings and drawings collected together by Reynolds and illustrating many mechanical contrivances in the Coalbrookdale Coalfield. Some are signed by Thomas Telford. Illustrated here is the section of the Hollins Wood Blast Engine.

Col: Science Museum, London.

Lit: H. W. Dickinson, 'An 18th Century Engineer's Sketchbook', *Transactions of the Newcomen Society*, vol II, 1921.

46. *Hay Inclined Plane, 1819*

From Jean Dutens, *Mémoires sur les Travaux Publiques d'Angleterre* (1819).

A detailed engineering drawing of the mechanism at the top of the Hay inclined plane for transferring tub boats between the top level of the Shropshire Canal and the lower level at the Coalport Basin.

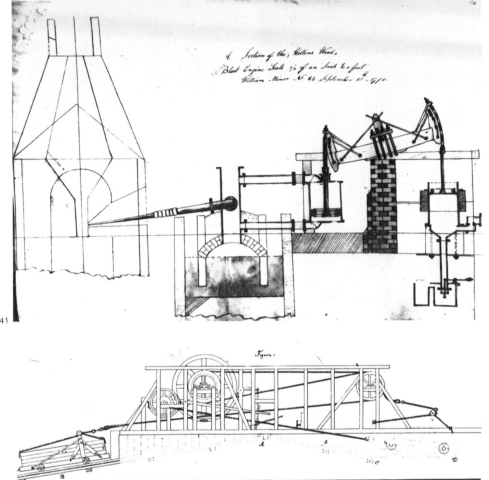

A Section of the ; Collins Wood,
Blast Engine Scale ⅛ of an Inch to a foot
William Miner No 14 September 17 1795.

45

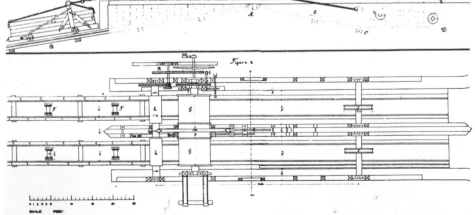

46

47. *Inclined railways at Coalport, 1819* (not illustrated)
From Jean Dutens, *Mémoires sur les Travaux Publiques d'Angleterre* (1819).

48

48. W. RADDON (active 1817–62) after S. LANE (1780–1859)
Thomas Telford
Engraving, 16 × 12 in (406 × 304 mm).
Inscribed, bottom 'THOˢ. TELFORD ESQ. F.R.S. L & E. / To the Vice Presidents, Members & Associates of the Incorporated Institution of Civil Engineers / This print of the President, from a painting by S. Lane in their possession / is dedicated with permission by their most obedient servants Edmd. Turrell & W. Raddon / London. Published January 10 1831 by Edmd. Turrell 46 Clarendon Street. Sommers Town. W. Raddon, 38 Sidmouth Street, Regent Square, and by the Sectry of the Institution of Civil Engineers, Buckingham Street, Strand.'; blc 'Painted by S. Lane.'; brc 'Engraved by W. Raddon.'.
Col: Elton Collection, Ironbridge Gorge Museum Trust.

49. JOSEPH MALLORD WILLIAM TURNER, RA (1775–1851)
The Limekiln at Coalbrookdale (see p 42)
Oil on board, 11¾ × 15⅞ in (274 × 400 mm).
Col: J. Chalon (when engraved, the picture was in the possession of Mr J. Chalon – probably the artist John James Chalon, 1778–1854); P. Potter (sold at Mrs Potter's Sale, Christie's 1909 – purchased Agnew); W. Lockett; Agnew, sold Christie's 7 June 1918 (70 – purchased J. Walford); D. F. Ward, Hove; Sotheby's 1966, purchased Mellon Collection.

Lit: Sir Walter Armstrong, *Turner*, 1902, p 220; Klingender 1947, p 102, fig 27; Klingender 1968, p 206, fig 27.
Ex: *J. M. W. Turner*, National Gallery of Art, Washington, DC, 31 October 1968 – 21 April 1969 (2 repr).

Little needs to be said of the widely documented life of Turner. He was admitted to the RA schools in 1789 and exhibited there for the first time in 1791. His genius was recognized by the RA who supported him in the face of bitter criticism from many of his contemporaries. He was made a full Academician in 1802.

In the 1790s Turner worked for the great art patron Dr Munro, where he worked with Girtin, with whom he is often compared in these early years. Up to *c* 1796 Turner's work was almost exclusively made up of topographical watercolours. However, in 1796 or '97 he exhibited two oil paintings at the RA. *The Limekiln at Coalbrookdale* dates from these early years of oil painting. The composition is lit by the glare from the kiln although the kiln itself is hidden from view by a dark bank in the middle distance. We can see Turner's interest in light effects beginning to develop here, an interest which was to culminate in works devoted purely to light.

50. FREDERICK CHRISTIAN LEWIS (1779–1856) after J. M. W. Turner (1775–1851)
Colebrook Dale
Mezzotint, 5⅞ × 7⅜ in (151 × 200 mm).
Inscribed, bc 'engraved from the original picture in the possession of Mr. J. Chalon by F. C. Lewis 5 Gt. Newport Street. published in July 1825, London, by Hurst Robinson & Co., 6 Pall Mall.'; brc 'PROOF.'
Col: Ironbridge Gorge Museum Trust.
Lit: W. G. Rawlinson, *The Engraved works of J. M. W. Turner, R.A.*, 1913, II, p 374, no 775; Klingender, 1947, pp 81, 176, fig 15.
Ex: Manchester 1968 (209).

For a complete list of the states of this mezzotint see Rawlinson.

51. J. BAKER
Iron Bridge near Coalbrook-dale
Aquatint, 5 × 6½ in (127 × 165 mm).
Inscribed, bc 'Iron Bridge near Coalbrookdale'; brc 'R. Hancock fc'; blc 'J. Baker delin.'
Col: Morley Tonkin (34), Ironbridge Gorge Museum Trust.

Baker was an etcher in Islington towards the end of the 18th century. He specialised in

50

51

52a

52b

portraits and illustrations. He did much magazine work, especially for *The European Magazine*. This engraving is copied directly from T. F. Burney's engraving (25).

52   SIR RICHARD COLT HOARE (1758–1838)
(a)   *Iron Bridge, Colebrook Dale*
Pencil, $9\frac{1}{4} \times 10\frac{5}{8}$ in (235×270 mm).
Inscribed, tlc 'Iron Bridge, Colebrook Dale'; blc 'Colt Hoare deln'.
Col: Cardiff Public Library. Sketch book, vol 1, p 12.

The artist was not alone in finding it difficult to draw the Iron Bridge and a second attempt is seen in the top of the sketch.

(b)   *Colebrook Dale*
Pencil, $9 \times 11\frac{7}{8}$ in (229×302 mm).
Inscribed tlc and trc 'Colebrook Dale'.
Col: Cardiff Public Library. Sketch book, vol 1, p 8.

The sketch probably depicts Rose Cottages and the malthouse and cottages which used to stand above them.

49

53, 54. SAMUEL IRELAND (d 1800)
53. *Iron Bridge near Coalbrook Dale*
Colour lithograph, $4\frac{3}{8} \times 6\frac{1}{2}$ in (106 × 165 mm).
Inscribed, bc 'IRON BRIDGE NEAR COALBROOK-
DALE, Pub. by G. & W. B. Whittaker, Ave
Maria Lane'; blc 'Sam. Ireland del.'; brc 'F
Calvert, Lithog.'.
From Thomas Harral, *Picturesque Views of the
Severn*, 1824, vol 1, p 230.
Col: Morley Tonkin (37), Ironbridge Gorge
Museum Trust.

53

54. *Buildwas Bridge*
Colour lithograph, $5 \times 6\frac{3}{4}$ in (127 × 172 mm).
Inscribed, bc 'Bildewas Bridge / London,
published by G. & W. B. Whittaker: Ave
Maria Lane'; blc 'Sam. Ireland Del.'; brc 'F
Calvert lithog.'.
Col: Morley Tonkin (68), Ironbridge Gorge
Museum Trust.
Lit: B. Trinder, *Extraordinary District*, 1977, p
43; B. Trinder, *The Industrial Revolution*, p. 191.

This view of the bridge was drawn before the
reconstruction of 1795 by Thomas Telford (see
item 43), but probably shows some of the
preliminary works.
Samuel Ireland, the engraver, came from Wem
and was responsible for the plates in Thomas
Harral's book. Ireland's visit to Coalbrookdale

54

was probably some time in the 1790s and his description of a blast furnace is the best that is known for the Severn Gorge.

55. W. SCARROTT
Iron Bridge
Engraving, $3\frac{7}{8} \times 5\frac{5}{8}$ in (99 × 143 mm), inscribed, bc 'Iron Bridge, / Erected over the River SEVERN, near Coalbrook Dale in the County of Salop' with a description of the bridge; below, 'SHIFNAL, printed by W. Scarrott.'.
Col: Salop County Record Office 140/47.

The description to Scarrott's plate, which incidentally was almost certainly copied from the view by T. F. Burney (item 25), describes the bridge in the following terms. 'This amazing Structure, was cast at Coalbrook Dale in the year 1778, and erected in the years 1779 and 1780. The expansion of the Arch is 90 feet within, and its height 40 feet, which, with the additional height of the Walls it is supported on, makes it near 50 feet from the Water; The Road over the top is 10 yards wide and one hundred in length, covered with strong iron plates. The Whole Bridge is computed to contain 378 Tons of Iron.'

55

56. MATHEW DUBOURG (fl 1786–1825)
The Cast Iron Bridge near Coalbrookdale
Aquatint, $17\frac{1}{4} \times 23\frac{5}{8}$ in. (438 × 600 mm).
Inscribed, bc 'The CAST IRON BRIDGE over the RIVER SEVERN near COALBROOKDALE. / London 1823, published by J. Taylor at the Architectural Library 59 High Holborn.'; brc 'Engd by M. Dubourg, 1 Buxton Place, Lambeth'.
Col: Ironbridge Gorge Museum Trust.
Lit: Klingender 1947, p 88; Klingender 1968, p 76.

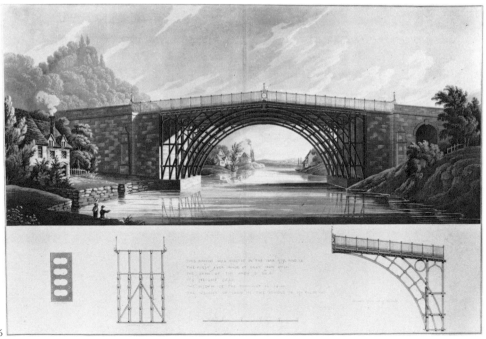

56

Although published in 1823, the engraving must have been done many years earlier as it shows the bridge with stone land arches. It is drawn from the same viewpoint as Rooker's (item 15), but is more accurately detailed. Dubourg was a skilful and very adaptable engraver. He exhibited miniatures at the RA in 1786, 1797 and 1808, and engraved landscapes after Claude. He illustrated volumes of classical archaeology and gothic architecture but also made drawings of a more engineering nature, as can be seen here.

57. CHARLES DIBDIN (1745–1814)
Coalbrookdale
Engraving, $7\frac{1}{4} \times 8\frac{3}{4}$ in (184 × 222 mm).
Inscribed, bc 'London, published by Mr Dibdin, 1801'; trc '9'.
Col: Morley Tonkin (18), Ironbridge Gorge Museum Trust.
Lit: *Country Life*, 3 Nov 1977, pp 1276–7.

Dibdin was a popular song writer in his day, and with the proceeds from the sale of his songs he set himself up as a printer and publisher. He wrote and illustrated his own books, having the original pictures engraved. In 1801–2 he published *Observations on a Tour through almost the whole of England and part of Scotland*, in which *Coalbrookdale* was reproduced (pl 9). Dibdin was an actor as well as an artist and was a friend of the Forester family at Willey.

> I went to see COALBROOK DALE. I found the country beautifully picturesque, and if I could have satisfied my hunger by the food I took in at my eyes, I should have had no reason to complain.
> It was our intention I remember to stay all night, but this was impossible, for the day was insufferably hot, and the prodigious piles of coal burning to coke, the furnaces, the forges, and other tremendous objects emitting fire and smoke to an immense extent, together with the intolerable stench of the sulphur, approached very nearly to an idea of being placed in an air-pump. We were therefore glad enough to go away and sleep at SHEFNAL. By this time it was evening, and the effect produced in Plate IX, introduced in the First Volume, for which a reason will be given at the end of the work, is a pretty faithful portraiture of the surrounding scenery.
> Affected as we were with the thick atmosphere, if it may be called so, in this strange region, we nevertheless noted some of its most remarkable objects, and among them of course the iron bridge which was then a great curiosity to me, as I had at that time never seen that at BRIDGEWATER, or the other at SUNDERLAND. I think this is the most beautiful of the three; for though it seems like network wrought in iron, it will apparently last uninjured for ages. COALBROOKDALE wants nothing but Cerberus to give you an idea of the heathen hell. The Severn may pass for the Styx, with this difference, that CHARON, turned turn-pike-man, ushers you over the bridge instead of rowing in his crazy boat; the men and women might easily be mistaken for devils and furies, and the entrance of any one of those blazing caverns, where they polish the cylinders, for TARTARUS; and, really, if an atheist, who had never heard of COLEBROOK DALE, could be transported there in a dream, and left to awake at the mouth of one of those furnaces, surrounded on all sides by such a number of infernal objects, though he has been all his life the most profligate un-believer that ever added blasphemy to incredulity, he would infallibly tremble at the just judgment that in imagination would appear to await him.

57

44

A View from the Iron Bridge
Exhibition Notes

The cast-iron ribs of the world's first iron bridge met across the River Severn on 2 July 1779. To celebrate the bicentenary of this important and graceful structure, which stands today as one of the supreme symbols of the Industrial Revolution, the Ironbridge Gorge Museum Trust has brought together a unique collection of works depicting the bridge and its environs for exhibition at the Royal Academy of Arts from 25 August to 18 November 1979, under the title *A View from the Iron Bridge*.

As a result of the events which took place in the Severn Gorge around Coalbrookdale the area has been called the Birthplace of the Industrial Revolution. Here Abraham Darby first smelted iron ore with coke instead of charcoal in 1709. The success and confidence of the Shropshire ironmasters was epitomised seventy years later by the construction of the cast-iron bridge of 100 feet 6 inches span, which was quickly to become a focus for travellers from all over the world. The impact of industry and technology on the landscape attracted many artists who found inspiration not only in the bridge and its spectacular setting but also in the drama of the furnaces, mines and machinery. This interest has continued and the exhibition includes several twentieth century works.

Paintings, drawings and engravings have been drawn from public and private collections in Britain and America, as well as commemorative items in ceramics, glass and iron. Looking beyond the panache and daring of the bridge itself, the exhibition reviews the subsequent development of this part of industrial Britain, and goes on to draw parallels with other parts of the country, in particular where mining and ironmaking were important before 1830.

The Museum's publication *A View from the Iron Bridge,* is a definitive list of the images of the 1779 Iron Bridge and its immediate surroundings. Details of all other works on display are set out below.

For various reasons several works listed in the catalogue will not be on display at the exhibition.

Footnotes / corrections

P.7 The caption at the top of the page should read . . . by Newman and Company c.1842. The bottom caption is a detail of catalogue No. 17.

P.20 Catalogue No. 14:
Since the compilation of the catalogue it has become clear that this work is a copy of the engraving (catalogue No. 17) after the watercolour and not a study for it.

P.22 Catalogue No. 17:
This engraving is not hand-coloured.

P.30 Catalogue No. 30:
This engraving is not hand-coloured.

P.35 Catalogue No. 39:
Note the inclined plane in the background on the right hand side of the portrait.

P.40 Catalogue No. 48:
Note Telford's Pontcysyllte aqueduct in the background on the left hand side of the portrait.

P.70 Catalogue No. 121:
The image of Nash's painting is reversed.

The Ironbridge Gorge Museum Trust has also collaborated with Asa Briggs on the recent publication of a major book *Iron Bridge to Crystal Palace — Impact and Images of the Industrial Revolution*, which includes illustrations of many of the works on display. It serves to set the exhibition in the wider context of the Industrial Revolution. The book is published by Thames & Hudson, price £7.50.

Additional Works in the Exhibition

125. PREBEN HANSEN (b 1908)
The cast iron bridge at Coalbrookdale near Wellington, April 1947
Pencil, ink and crayon, 13 × 5$\frac{1}{16}$ in (333 × 386 mm).
Col: Artist's collection.
An upstream view of the Iron Bridge from the Broseley side of the River Severn.

126. JOSEPH WRIGHT of Derby (1734-97)
An Iron Forge
Oil on canvas, 48 × 52 in (1219 × 1321 mm).
Signed and dated on stone slab, br 'Jo Wright/Pinx.ᵛ1772'.
Col: Admiral of the Fleet the Earl Mountbatten of Burma (from Broadlands opening exhibition).
Typical of Wright's work in its concentration on the source of light as the central theme, it shows a small forge of the period with a water-driven tilt-hammer. The painting was mezzotinted by Richard Earlom and published by Boydell, 1 January 1773. Another version of an iron forge, seen from without, is in the Hermitage Museum, Leningrad.

127. PAUL SANDBY (1725-1809)
The Iron Forge between Dolgelli and Barmouth in Merionethshire
Aquatint, 9$\frac{5}{16}$ × 12$\frac{3}{8}$ in (237 × 315 mm).
Published by Paul Sandby, London, 1 September 1776.
Col: Elton Collection, Ironbridge Gorge Museum Trust.
Views in North Wales, of which this picture is plate XVIII, was the first book issued in aquatint in England and reproduced wash drawings made by Sandby between 1775-6. It is typical of early aquatints to be published in monochrome, in this case sepia; colour was added only to later editions. Paul Sandby was the leading topographical artist of the second half of the eighteenth century, introducing direct observation into his work in contrast to the contrived prospects of his predecessors and the picturesque invention of the romantic movement which followed.

128. JULIUS CAESAR IBBETSON (1759-1817)
Interior of Cyfarthfa Ironworks
Watercolour, 8$\frac{5}{8}$ × 11$\frac{13}{16}$ in (218 × 300 mm).
Col: Merthyr Tydfil Borough Council.
Ibbetson is known to have visited Wales in 1789 and 1792. This work probably dates from this period.

129. JOSEPH MALLORD WILLIAM TURNER (1775-1851)
Cyfarthfa Ironworks from the Brecon Road
Pencil drawing, 11$\frac{1}{4}$ × 18 in (285 × 457 mm).
Inscribed brc 'Carfara Works from Brecon Road'.
Col: British Museum.
A page from the dismembered 'Cyfarthfa' sketch-book, dated 1798 by A. J. Finberg.

130. THOMAS HORNOR (active 1800-44)
Rolling Mills, Merthyr Tydfil
Pen, ink and grey wash, 11$\frac{3}{4}$ × 19$\frac{1}{4}$ in (299 × 488 mm).
Col: Elton Collection, Ironbridge Gorge Museum Trust.
Between 1817-19, Hornor produced albums of *Views of South Wales* for wealthy patrons, interspersing romantic landscapes with scenes of industrial activity along the Vale of Neath. The furnaces and iron foundries of Merthyr Tydfil shook Hornor out of his usual style to produce this angular picture in which the shafts of light criss-cross the sky. A pair of two-high rolls can be seen at the extreme right and many of the end products of the works are visible in the form of flat rods and bars.

131. JAMES SANDS (active 1811-41) after THOMAS ALLOM (1804-72)
Lymington Ironworks, on the Tyne
Engraving, 5$\frac{1}{2}$ × 7$\frac{7}{8}$ in (140 × 200 mm).
Published by Fisher, Son & Co, London 1835.
Col: Elton Collection, Ironbridge Gorge Museum Trust.
The engraving was intended to show contemporaries the horrors of industrialisation, although its value now lies in its depiction of the working of an iron furnace. One can see blast furnaces for the production of cast-iron, waggons being hauled up inclines with raw materials and the tall cementation furnaces for the production of steel.

132. ROBERT NOYES (1780-1843)
View of numerous furnaces and pumping or winding engines
Watercolour, 11 × 17 in (279 × 432 mm).
Signed and dated, brc: '1827 R. Noyes'.
Col: The Trustees of the William Salt Library, Stafford.
The scene is believed to be Wilkinson's first Staffordshire ironworks at Bradley. The artist is associated with Wolverhampton where he was for a time drawing master at the art school.

133. JAMES SHARPLES (1825-92)
The Forge
Oil on canvas 36$\frac{1}{2}$ × 51$\frac{1}{4}$ in (927 × 1302 mm).

Col: Miss Marion Sharples, on permanent loan to Blackburn Museum & Art Gallery. Painted between 1844 and 1847 'The Forge' is Sharples' most important work, executed in his spare time while working in a Bury foundry. He later engraved the work on steel.

134. ANON
Wednesbury by Night
Oil on canvas, 38½ × 63 in (943 × 1543 mm).
Col: Ironbridge Gorge Museum Trust.
The picture, probably dating from the mid-nineteenth century, depicts a group of blast furnaces in the Black Country around Wednesbury. In the foreground can be seen pit heaps and the coking of coal.
Purchased from the Forest Glen Appeal.

135-6. ALFRED WILLIAM HUNT (1830-96)
135. *Iron Works Middlesbrough*
Oil on canvas, 17¼ × 25¼ in (438 × 641 mm).
Col: The Trustees of the Tate Gallery.

136. *Middlesbrough, tapping the furnaces*
Wash drawing, 11⅛ × 15¼ in (283 × 387 mm).
Col: Elton Collection, Ironbridge Gorge Museum Trust.
Hunt is known primarily for his watercolours. This painting and the study for it show the running of molten iron into pig beds (also seen in no 32) with Turneresque treatment of the light. They are thought to have been executed circa 1865 to 70.

137. BRITISH SCHOOL (c1780)
Portrait of a gentleman holding a drawing of a steam engine
Oil on canvas, 32½ × 27⅞ in (826 × 708 mm).
Col; Elton Collection, Ironbridge Gorge Museum Trust.
The steam engine is an atmospheric engine of the Newcomen type, with a heavy beam. First used in about 1710, 104 engines are known to have been built by 1733, and possibly as many as 1000 by the end of the eighteenth century. In 1968 the portrait was dated c1780 by Anne Buck, from details of dress.

138. JOHN HASSELL (1767-1825)
Coalworks
Watercolour, 8¹¹⁄₁₆ × 13¼ in (224 × 336 mm).
Signed and dated 1791.
Col: Elton Collection, Ironbridge Gorge Museum Trust.
John Hassell was one of many topographical artists of the late eighteenth century who introduced decrepit industrial features in their work as 'picturesque deformities'. The picturesque school allowed the inclusion of engines, mills and mines, if they were made to appear worn out and ancient and therefore representing no threat to natural beauty and the status quo. Sir Arthur Elton suggested Glamorganshire as the location of this scene.

139. ANON
Pit-head of a Coal Mine with steam winding gear
Oil on canvas, 37⅝ × 60¼ in (955 × 1530 mm).
Col: Walker Art Gallery, Liverpool.
The scene includes a Newcomen engine adapted to winding. The steam engine was occasionally used in this way from the late eighteenth century until well into the nineteenth, applied to shallow pits. (c1820).

140. JOSEPH CLEMENT (1779-1844)
A Newcomen engine
Pen, ink and grey wash, 15¾ × 18₁₆ in (400 × 465 mm).
Col: Elton Collection, Ironbridge Gorge Museum Trust.
The original of an engraving by Edward Kennion (1744-1809) in Charles Frederick Partington's *An Historical and Descriptive Account of the Steam Engine,* published in 1822. Clement's drawings were also engraved by George Gladwyn for use in Thomas Tredgold's *The Steam Engine,* published in 1827.
Clement was a fine draughtsman working first for Joseph Bramah and then for Henry Maudslay. He designed and built precision tools, notably the first planing machine, and did much to develop accurate screw-cutting dies and taps.

141. J RAFFIELD (active 1797-1825) after ROBERT CLARK
East View of the cast-iron bridge over the River Wear, at Sunderland, previous to the centre being taken down
Aquatint, 17₁₆ × 29₁₆ in (437 × 738 mm) 1795.
Col: Elton Collection, Ironbridge Gorge Museum Trust.
This print is dedicated to Rowland Burdon, Member of Parliament for Sunderland. He was also director of Walker's, the Rotherham iron foundry that built the bridge and patentee for this type of construction. In this view of the second major iron bridge the masonry piers are shown built only up to the springing of the cast-iron voussoirs. The height of the bridge and the timber centring shown in place still allowed passage for the tall-masted ships, as the Admiralty insisted. It was completed in 1796.

142.   PETER NICHOLSON (1765-1844)
A South East View of Sunderland Bridge
Aquatint, hand coloured, $13\frac{3}{4}$ × 18 in (347 × 457 mm).
Signed and dated, brc 'Nicholson 1798'.
Col: Ironbridge Gorge Museum Trust.

143.   WILSON LOWRY after THOMAS MALTON (1745-1804)
A Perspective view of the Design for a cast-iron bridge, consisting of a single arch 600 feet in the span and calculated to supply the place of the present London Bridge
Engraving in line and aquatint, $21\frac{9}{16}$ × $47\frac{1}{16}$ in (548 × 1198 mm).
Col: Telford Development Corporation.
Malton, who was responsible for the aquatinting, was an architectural draughtsman. One of Turner's masters, he executed many watercolours and aquatints of London. Telford's design for a single-span cast-iron bridge, 600 feet across, was published in 1801. The scheme was abandoned because of difficulties in purchasing enough land for the high approaches.

144.   S RUSSELL (active mid-nineteenth century)
Britannia Tubular Bridge over the Menai Straits during its construction in 1848
Published by S Russell, London 1849.
Hand-coloured lithograph, $22\frac{3}{8}$ × 30 in (568 × 763 mm).
Col: Elton Collection, Ironbridge Gorge Museum Trust.
The Britannia Bridge was designed by Robert Stephenson in the form of a rigid tubular or box girder, inside which the trains ran. It is an important structure in the history of civil engineering being the first in which there was any systematic testing of the materials used. The tubes were built on the Caernarvon shore, floated into position and raised to the top of the piers by hydraulic rams. The bridge cost the Chester & Holyhead Railway Company £600,000 but carried traffic from its opening in 1849 until being destroyed by fire in 1970. The present bridge still uses the abutments of the Britannia Bridge.

145.   GEORGE HAWKINS (1810-52) after JAMES WILSON CARMICHAEL (1800-68)
High Level Bridge, Newcastle upon Tyne
Published by E. G. J. Bruce, Newcastle, 1849.
Hand-tinted lithograph, $17\frac{3}{8}$ × $21\frac{1}{2}$ in (440 × 545 mm).
Col: Elton Collection, Ironbridge Gorge Museum Trust.
The high level bridge at Newcastle upon Tyne was

designed by Robert Stephenson with John Dobson and completed in 1849. It carried a road below and railway tracks above, enabling trains to travel across the Tyne for the first time. The bowstring girders were of cast-iron raised on five stone piers 146 feet above the River Tyne. Hawkins established himself as an architectural engineer and lithographer in the 1840s. Klingender compared his work favourably with that of John Cooke Bourne.

146.   THOMAS VALENTINE ROBINS
The Opening of the Royal Albert Bridge, Saltash, 1859
Oil on canvas, $17\frac{7}{16}$ × $19\frac{5}{8}$ in (291 × 497 mm).
Col: Elton Collection, Ironbridge Gorge Museum Trust.
The Saltash Bridge which took the South Devon Railway across the River Tamar was the last work of Isambard Kingdom Brunel. The crossing of the Tamar was the most formidable barrier to the westward progress of the railway as 1000 feet of water had to be bridged at a height of 100 feet to meet Admiralty stipulations about clearance for shipping. The problem was solved by supporting the bridge deck from wrought-iron tubes of elliptical section. The bridge was opened on 2 May 1859.
The Royal Yacht Britannia is seen passing the bridge with Prince Albert raising his hat in salute from the ship. The locomotive, seen approaching the bridge from the left, drew a specially prepared platform truck on which lay the dying Brunel, too weak to participate in any other way.

147-8.   ROBERT HAVELL after GEORGE WALKER (1781-1856)
147.   *Factory Children*
Aquatint, hand-coloured, $7\frac{7}{8}$ × $11\frac{7}{8}$ in (200 × 300 mm).
Published in Leeds 1814.
Col: Elton Collection, Ironbridge Gorge Museum Trust.

148.   ROBERT and GEORGE HAVELL (active 1812-37) after GEORGE WALKER
The Collier
Aquatint, hand-coloured, $9\frac{3}{4}$ × $14\frac{1}{4}$ in (248 × 363 mm).
Published in Leeds 1813.
Col: Elton Collection, Ironbridge Gorge Museum Trust.
Both prints appeared in *The Costume of Yorkshire* published by Robinson & Sons of Leeds: 'The Collier' being Plate III and 'Factory Children' Plate XXXVI.
The publication first appeared as ten parts, issued

1813-14, and as a single volume shortly afterwards. Forty aquatints were published covering the workers, artisans, craftsmen, labourers and paupers of Yorkshire. The two children stand before a textile mill, an industry notorious for its use of child labour; the collier stands in front of a steam engine and pithead gear. The locomotive was built by John Blenkinsop (1783-1831) in 1812. The scene: Charles Brandling's Middleton Colliery near Leeds.

149-51. JOSEPH NASH (1808-78)
149. *The Inauguration*
Chromolithograph, 24⅛ × 30¾ in (620 × 781 mm).
Col: Elton Collection, Ironbridge Gorge Museum Trust.

150. *The Foreign Nave*
Chromolithograph, 25 × 30½ in (636 × 775 mm).
Col: Elton Collection, Ironbridge Gorge Museum Trust.
These two chromolithographs form a pair. They are similar in style to but much larger than the chromolithographs in Dickinsons' *Comprehensive Pictures of the Great Exhibition of 1851.*
The Crystal Palace was designed by Joseph Paxton (1801-65). Its importance as a building lies largely in its use of iron and glass on such a scale, in the astounding speed and simplicity of erection and in the combination of these factors to produce an aesthetically pleasing design. The Crystal Palace was 1848 feet long, 408 feet wide and 108 feet high and yet was built in only five months. The exhibition was opened on 1 May and closed on 11 October 1851 after the incredible number of 6,039,195 visitors had passed through its turnstiles. This 'temporary' structure in Hyde Park was dismantled in 1854 and re-erected at Sydenham, where it remained until being destroyed by fire on 30 November 1936.

151. *The Closing of the Great Exhibition*
Pencil and water colour, heightened in white, 19 × 25½ in (483 × 648 mm).
Col: Elton Collection, Ironbridge Gorge Museum Trust.
This is an unused study for Dickinsons' *Comprehensive Pictures of the Great Exhibition of 1851,* published 1851-3.
The ceremony was performed by Prince Albert, sitting at the head of the table, in the centre of the picture. Note the Coalbrookdale gates in the background.

152. OWEN JONES (1809-1874)
St Pancras Station and Hotel, competition design, 1865
Pen, ink and water colour, 20⅟₆ × 37⅜ in (510 × 950 mm).
Col: Elton Collection, Ironbridge Gorge Museum Trust.
Owen Jones was Superintendent of Works during the construction of the Crystal Palace. In 1865 he submitted a design for the station, which according to contemporary accounts, differed from those of the other competitors in so far as the hotel was made subsidiary to the shed. St Pancras, which was opened in stages from about 1869, was designed by Sir George Gilbert Scott (1811-78), architect and W H Barlow (1812-1902), engineer.

A View from the Iron Bridge
General Information

Dates of exhibition: 25 August to 18 November 1979
Hours of opening: Daily 10am to 6pm
Price of admission: 90p (adults), 50p (students, children and OAP's)
Half price Sunday morning
Illustrated catalogue. (Price £1.95)

Visitors are required to deposit all miscellaneous items other than ladies' handbags with the attendants at the Cloakrom in the Entrance Hall. The other attendants are strictly forbidden to take charge of anything.
Invalids may use their own wheeled chairs or obtain the use of one without charge by previous arrangement. Application should be made to the Registry for the necessary authority.
Buffet restaurant and licensed bar. Open daily: Access is from the ground floor Entrance Hall.

The Ironbridge Gorge Museum Trust

The Ironbridge Gorge Museum Trust is an independent charitable organisation which was formed in 1967 to preserve the outstanding remains of industry in the Severn Gorge in Telford, Shropshire and to present and interpret them to the public. Over the last decade the Trust has been engaged in restoring the monuments of this 'Cradle of the Industrial Revolution' and is now visited by over 200,000 visitors each year. In 1977 the Museum won the Museum of the Year Award and in 1978 it was named the first European Museum of the Year. Recently the bicentenary of the Iron Bridge has been celebrated with the opening of the new Museum of Iron, Coalbrookdale by HRH The Prince of Wales.

The President of the Museum Trust is Lady Labouchere a descendant of the Darbys of Coalbrookdale. The Trust's Chairman is Mr T. F Honess CBE, and its Director is Dr Neil Cossons. The Museum Trust, which from the outset has enjoyed the help and encouragement of Telford Development Corporation, is substantially self-supporting. Capital amounting to £1.6m, has been raised through the medium of the Ironbridge Gorge Museum Development Trust, set up specifically for this purpose under the presidency of Sir Montague Finniston FRS. The Development Trust's Chairman is Mr R. Sidaway and its London Committee is chaired by Lord Layton. Further funds are sought to continue the Museum's growth and development. For details write to the Development Trust Director, Ironbridge Gorge Museum Development Trust, Ironbridge, Telford, Salop TF8 7AW (095-245) 3522.

Major Donors

Annual Subscriber Scheme
Barton Conduits Limited
Birmid Qualcast Limited
British Rolling Mills Limited
British Steel Corporation
Brockhouse Limited
Edward Cadbury Trust
Carnegie United Kingdom Trust
W.A. Cadbury Trust
Carter Thermal Limited
Clearing Banks
Ernest Cook Trust
Countryside Commission
Darby & Company Limited
Dawley U.D.C.
Delta Metals Limited
Ductile Steels Limited
Dulverton Trust
Duport Group Limited
Department of Education and Science
Department of the Environment
Ever Ready Company Limited
Friends of the Museum
G.K.N. Limited
Glynwed Limited
Hayward Foundation
Historic Buildings Council
Lady Labouchere
Landmark Trust
Leach 14th Trust
Leche Trust
L.C.P. Holdings Limited
Lilleshall Group Limited

Lowe and Fletcher Limited
Lyndale Limited
Manpower Services Commission
Sir Alfred McAlpine Limited
McLechnie Brothers Limited
John McLean and Sons Limited
Midland News Association
Area Museum and Art Gallery Service for
   the Midlands
National Coal Board
Pilgrim Trust
The Rt. Hon. The Earl of Plymouth
Quinton Hazell Limited
Radcliffe Trust
Reg Morton Ironworks Fund
Rolls-Royce Motors Limited (Shrewsbury)
Rubery Owen Company Limited
Salop County Council
Science Museum
Serck Limited
Sheerness Steel Limited
Staveley Industries Limited
Tarmac Limited
Telford Development Corporation
Thornton Baker and Company
Thyssen (GB) Limited
Tube Investments Limited
Victoria and Albert Museum
Walker Trust
Walmsleys and Son Limited
William Whittingham Limited
Wrekin District Council

Royal Academy of Arts
Programme of Exhibitions 1979

A View from the Iron Bridge   25 August-18 November
organised by the Ironbridge Gorge Museum Trust

Horses of San Marco   8 September-28 October
sponsored by British Olivetti

Burlington International Fine Art Fair   28 September-12 October
presented in arrangement with The Burlington Magazine

John Flaxman, RA — Mythology and Industry   26 October-9 December
sponsored by Wedgwood, with additional support from
the Arts Council of Great Britain

Post-Impressionism   17 November-16 March
generously supported by IBM UK Limited

Further details of these exhibitions and details of the Friends of the Royal Academy may be
obtained from the Press Office — telephone (01) 734 9052.
Business Art Galleries, selling, renting and leasing contemporary art, open Monday to Friday
from 9.30 am to 6.00 pm — telephone (01) 734 1448.

The Friends of the Royal Academy

Patron: H.R.H. The Duke of Edinburgh, K.G., K.T.

Friends
£10 annually or £7 annually for Museum Staff, Teachers, Pensioners and Young Friends
(16-25)
Gain free and immediate admission to all Royal Academy Exhibitions with a guest or husband/
wife and children under 16.
Obtain catalogues at a reduced price.
Enjoy the privacy of the Friends' Room in Burlington House.
Receive Private View invitations to various exhibitions including the Summer Exhibition.
Have access to the Library and Historical Archives.
Benefit from other special arrangements, such as lectures and tours.
Artist Subscribers
£17.50 annually
Receive all the privileges shown above.
Receive free submission forms for the Summer Exhibition.
Obtain art materials at a reduced price.
Obtain constructive help where the experience of the Royal Academy could be of assistance.
Sponsors
£500 (corporate)
£100 (individual)
annually
Receive all the privileges offered to Friends.
Enjoy the particular privileges of reserving the Royal Academy's Private Rooms when
appropriate and similarly of arranging evening viewings of certain exhibitions.
Receive acknowledgement through the inclusion of the Sponsor's name on official documents.
Benefactors
£1,000 or more.
An involvement with the Royal Academy which will be honoured in every way.
Further information is available from The Secretary, The Friends of the Royal Academy.

Benefactors and Sponsors of the Royal Academy of Arts

58

58, 59.   CORNELIUS VARLEY (1781–1873)
58.   *On the Severn at Coalbrookdale*
Pencil, 9¾ × 15⅞ in (247 × 403 mm).
Inscribed, blc 'In Colebrook Dale'.
Col: Fine Art Society 1974 (84), purchased by
the Friends of the Ironbridge Gorge Museum.
Lit: Michael Pidgley, 'Cornelius Varley,

Cotman and the Graphic Telescope', *Burlington Magazine*, Nov 1972, pp 781–6.

The viewpoint is doubtful, possibly Bedlam Furnaces on the left and the Calcutts on the right bank, since a horse-gin is shown close to the river on the right bank.

59

59.   *The Iron Bridge at Coalbrookdale*
Engraving, hand coloured, 6½ × 10 in
(165 × 254 mm).
Inscribed, bc 'The Iron Bridge at Colebrook
Dale'; blc 'C. Varley del.'; brc 'S. Porter,
printed by Richard Philips, 6 New Bridge
Street, Blackfriars.'; tc 'BRIDGES'.
Col: Ironbridge Gorge Museum Trust.

With his more famous brother John, the artist
was a founder of the Old Watercolour Society.
He made sketching tours with Cotman and
Joshua Cristall, although he was not really a
professional artist; he was rather a maker of
scientific instruments, but the large numbers of

his early watercolours that have quite recently
been rediscovered show him to be a talented
artist. He studied and copied works by John
Robert Cozens at Dr Munro's and learned from
here the method of underpainting in grey,
which enabled him to produce unusual atmospheric qualities. His invention, the Graphic
Telescope, a kind of camera lucida, is probably
more responsible for Varley's name being remembered today than are his artistic endeavours.
Varley toured Wales in 1802 when these
sketches were probably executed, as the bridge
is shown with stone abutments.

60

60–4. PHILIP JAMES DE LOUTHERBOURG
(1740–1812)
60. *Coalbrookdale by Night*
Oil on canvas, 26¾ × 42 in (680 × 1067 mm).
Signed, brc 'P. I. De Loutherbourg / R.A. 1801'
(second line above).
Col: Pictora Ltd, purchased by the Science
Museum, 1952.
Ex: RA 1801 (54, as 'A View of Colebrook
Dale by Night'); Manchester 1968 (32),
Washington, DC, *The Eye of Thomas Jefferson*,
1976 (113); Tate Gallery, *Landscape in Britain*,
1973 (133), repr p 73.

Of Alsatian descent, de Loutherbourg settled in
England in 1771 having already made a name
for himself in France as a court painter and a
member of the Paris Academy. Between 1773
and 1785, de Loutherbourg designed stage sets
for Garrick and Richard Brinsley Sheridan,
making an important contribution to the art of
stage design and stage mechanics. He became
well known for his ingenious effects in this
field, suggesting fire, sun, moonlight and
volcanic eruptions. The sense of movement,
the dramatic grouping and highly charged
emotional atmosphere that distinguished de
Loutherbourg's stage sets can also be seen in
his paintings of this period, of which many
were reproduced in aquatint.

The success of de Loutherbourg in the artistic
circles of this country is evident in his elections
as ARA in 1780, and full Academician the
following year. His continental baroque train-
ing helped him to acquire a mastery of the

dramatic, in a presentation which was far
removed from the classical serenity that still
dominated the English landscape school. The
rising generation of artists in this country were
searching for just the kind of dynamic emotional style that de Loutherbourg's work
represented, and his influence is evident in the
work of many young artists who were his
contemporaries.

De Loutherbourg found it equally easy to paint
in a picturesque style as in a sublime manner,
and the action in his works is usually de-
termined by some form of human activity.
Hence the dramatic appeal of the new industrial
landscape was especially intense to him, and it
was inevitable that he should come to visit the
Coalbrookdale area.

In 1801 he painted *Coalbrookdale by Night*, a
magnificently sublime representation of the
furnaces at Bedlam. Here we can see his
dramatic use of light and form combined to
produce an awe-inspiring view which is
acknowledged to be one of the finest industrial
paintings.

Recent comparison of this oil painting with
contemporary maps indicates that the group
of buildings to the left of the painting were
demolished to build the Ironbridge gas works
in the 1830s. The group on the right are the
furnaces proper with the smiths' shop and
joiners' shop nearest. Immediately behind this
building can be seen a tall engine house with
two chimneys and the furnace and casting
house are on the immediate right of the
illustration. The casting house ventilator can be

seen detailed in item 61. The flames and smoke which give the picture its impressive character are from the extensive coke hearths which were situated above the furnaces and which are also shown in the sketches by Farington and Munn. Iron castings in profusion lie around the scene and in the foreground a pair of horses are pulling a cart loaded with timber. The road used by this cart is still in use and forms part of the present Waterloo Street. Although plateways were used at Bedlam furnaces from an early date there is no evidence of their use in this painting or in the aquatint (item 65), after a drawing by de Loutherbourg.

61

62

63

64

65

61. *Fire Engine Coalbrookdale*
Pen and ink, $3\frac{1}{8} \times 4\frac{3}{4}$ in (79 × 121 mm).
Inscribed (verso) 'Fire Engine Coalbrookdale'.
Col: Perhaps acquired by Dr Munro from the artist; Dr Munro's sale, 27 June 1833 (110), bt Turner?; Turner Bequest, 1856 – BM (CCLXXII–47).
Lit: A. J. Finberg, *A Complete Inventory of the Drawings of the Turner Bequest*, 1909, II, 1223–5.
Ex: Manchester 1968 (211).

At the sale of Dr Munro, the great art patron, on 27 June 1833, lot 110 was described as 'By de Louterbourg. Sketches from nature in Wales; on cards in pen – ink. 44'. These drawings on small pieces of cardboard were among this lot and it is likely that they were bought by J. M. W. Turner, for they formed a part of the Turner Bequest in 1856.
Probably depicts a part of Bedlam Furnaces, particularly the boiler house and casting house.

62. *Largest Fire Engine of Coalbrookdale*
Pen and ink, $3\frac{1}{8} \times 4\frac{3}{4}$ in (79 × 121 mm).
Inscribed (verso) 'Largest fire Engin of Coalbrookdale'.
Col: same as 61; BM (CCLXXII–49).
Lit: same as 61.
Ex: Manchester 1968 (212).

Probably the Resolution Steam Engine. See also item 80, by J. Homes Smith.

63. *Large fire engine in Coalbrookdale*
Pen and ink, $3\frac{1}{8} \times 4\frac{3}{4}$ in. (79 × 121 mm).
Inscribed (verso) 'large fire engin in Coalbrookdale'.
Col: same as 61; BM (CCLXXII–45).
Lit: same as 61.
Ex: Manchester 1968 (213).

Like the previous item, this probably shows the Resolution Steam Engine, seen from the New Pool.

64. *Iron foundry, Madeley Wood*
Pen and ink, $3\frac{1}{8} \times 4\frac{3}{4}$ in (79 × 121 mm).
Inscribed (verso) 'Iron Foundery, Maidly Wood, on the top of the hill'.
Col: same as 61; BM (CCLXXII–48).
Lit: same as 61.

65. WILLIAM PICKETT (active 1792–1820)
after P. J. de Louterbourg (1740–1812)
Iron works, Coalbrookdale
Aquatint, hand coloured, $11\frac{7}{8} \times 14\frac{3}{8}$ in (303 × 364 mm).

Inscribed, below image, blc 'From the Original Drawing by P. I. DE LOUTHERBOURG, R.A.'; brc 'Published by R. BOWYER, Historical Gallery, Pall Mall, Jany. 1. 1805'; centre 'IRON WORK, COLEBROOK DALE'.
Col: Ironbridge Gorge Museum Trust.
Lit: Klingender 1947, p 77, repr pl III (colour); Klingender 1968, pp 99–100, 201, No. V, repr pl V (colour).
Ex: Manchester 1968 (229).

This work was aquatinted by William Pickett and coloured by John Clark for inclusion in de Louterbourg's *Romantic and Picturesque Scenery of England and Wales* (1805 and 1824). It could possibly have been a study for de Louterbourg's Eidophusikon – a dramatic representation of light and sound effects engineered by de Louterbourg in his own theatre. Pickett was a miscellaneous engraver of no great distinction. The scene depicts Bedlam Furnaces, viewed from downstream, and shows in the foreground a sledge being used to transport coal.

66. EDWARD DAYES (1763–1804)
Untitled
Monochrome wash, with indigo and indian ink, $9\frac{5}{8} \times 15\frac{1}{8}$ in (246 × 383 mm)
Col: BM (CCCLXXI–J; Turner Bequest).

This drawing bears strong resemblances to P. J. de Louterbourg's *Coalbrookdale by Night* (60), and also *Fire Engine, Coalbrookdale* (61); it almost certainly depicts Bedlam Furnaces.
Dayes is perhaps best known as the teacher of Girtin. He also influenced Turner's early work. He is noted for his architectural views and figure studies as well as for his landscapes.
Comparison of this sketch with a plan of Bedlam Furnaces by George Perry dated 1772 (BM – K. xxxvi.16.1) shows a direct correlation between buildings in plan and elevation. See Stuart B. Smith, 'New Light on the Bedlam Furnaces', *Historical Metallurgy*, vol 13, no 1, 1979, pp 21–30.

66

67–71. PAUL SANDBY MUNN (1773–1845)

67. *The Iron Bridge*

Pencil, 4⅞ × 9⅞ in (123 × 249 mm).

Signed, brc 'P. S. MUNN'; inscribed, blc 'Coalbrook. July 11th 1802 / after the starting of the bridge' (second line in a different hand); trc 'Madeley JULY 19'.

Col: Presented by the Venerable Archdeacon F. H. D. Smythe, 1948, to the V & A (E3112/1948).

Lit: S. D. Kitson, *The Life of John Sell Cotman*, 1937, p 41.

Ex: Manchester 1968 (221).

67

Munn was the godson of Paul Sandby and his early work shows Sandby's influence. He toured with Cotman in the summer of 1802, visiting the Coalbrookdale area on the way to Wales. His meticulous pencil drawings of the Iron Bridge (*Coalbrook July 11th 1802* and *Broseley July 11th 1802*) are particularly interesting as they show the bridge during the change from original stone abutment to the wooden arches that replaced it in part.

The starting of the bridge refers to the replacement of the solid stone abutments on the south bank with timber arches and allows one to date other illustrations with certainty.

68. *The Iron Bridge*

Pencil, 5¾ × 9¾ in (145 × 247 mm).

Signed, blc 'P. S. MUNN'; inscribed, brc 'Broseley July 11th 1802'; trc '18'.

Col: V & A (E214–1939).

To the right of the bridge are the stables, with cupola, for the Tontine Hotel, which were burnt down about 1817.

69. *Bedlam Furnace, Madeley Dale, Shropshire*

Watercolour, 12¾ × 21⅝ in (325 × 550 mm).

Inscribed, 'P S MUNN, 1803.'

Col: Mrs Judy Egerton.

Ex: RA 1803 (625); Tate Gallery, *Landscape in Britain*, 1973 (270).

The painting of *Bedlam Furnace, Madeley Dale, Shropshire* is dated 1803. As was usually the case, this finished painting was worked up from sketches made from the same spot from which de Loutherbourg painted his own very different view of Bedlam.

68

69

70

71

72

70. *Limekilns at Coalbrookdale, 1802*
Watercolour, $9\frac{1}{2} \times 14$ in (242×356 mm).
Col: S. D. Kitson, L. G. Duke, Morley Tonkin
Collection (Mrs Morley Tonkin).
Lit: S. D. Kitson, *The Life of John Sell Cotman*,
1937, p 41; Klingender 1947, p 101.

The limekilns shown are probably those that
remain on the present Wharfage, immediately
below Lincoln Hill and behind the Swan Inn.

71. *Great Wheel at Broseley, Salop*
Sepia tinted drawing, $8\frac{5}{8} \times 12\frac{7}{8}$ in (219×327
mm).
Inscribed (verso) 'Great Wheel, Broseley,
Shropshire.'
Col: Elton Collection, Ironbridge Gorge
Museum Trust.
Lit: *Shropshire Magazine*, December 1968.

The first illustration of Benthall water wheel
and corn mill. On the same tour, Munn also
sketched Buildwas Abbey and this was engraved by J. Greig for *The Beauties of England
and Wales*, 1803.

72–5. JOHN SELL COTMAN (1782–1842)
72. *Bedlam Furnace*
Watercolour, $10\frac{1}{4} \times 18\frac{3}{4}$ in (261×477 mm).
Col: Sir Hickman Bacon, Bt, Sir Edmund
Bacon, Bt.
Ex: Hull 1938 (4); Arts Council, *English Water
colours from the Hickman Bacon Collection*, 1946
(25); Norwich, *English Watercolours*, 1955 (51);

Manchester, Whitworth Art Gallery, *The
Norwich School*, 1961 (46); Manchester 1968
(143); Tate Gallery, *Landscape in Britain*, 1973
(263).
Lit: A. P. Oppé, 'The Water Colour Drawings
of John Sell Cotman', *Studio* Special Number,
1923, p viii; S. D. Kitson, *Life of John Sell
Cotman*, 1937, p 41, repr no 5; Klingender
1947, pp 80–1, 176, fig 14; D. Clifford,
Watercolours of the Norwich School, 1965, p xii,
repr pl 29b; Klingender 1968, pp 101–2, 201,
no VI, repr pl VI (colour).

Cotman is best known for his watercolours, in
which can be found some of the finest
landscapes of the early 19th century. Born in
Norwich, he later worked in London, until
1804, during which time he worked for Dr
Munro and eventually took over as the leader
of the Girtin Sketching Society. He exhibited at
the RA from 1800 to 1806 and his best work
depends on simple flat washes of colour and on
clearly defined almost geometric planes, start-
lingly modern in their design. On his return to
Norwich he became the leader of the Norwich
School of Painting.
The paintings of the Coalbrookdale area date
from his tour with Paul Sandby Munn in 1802,
a period when much of his best work was
produced. Munn and Cotman sat side by side as
they painted the same scenes, while producing
very different results, as can be seen in their
interpretation of Bedlam Furnace and Lincoln
Hill (cf items 69, 70).

73

73. *Coal Shaft at Coalbrookdale,* traditionally known as 'The Brick Kilns'
Pencil and wash, 8¾ × 13 in (222 × 330 mm), signed blc 'J S Cotman'.
Col: presented by Sir Michael Sadler, 1923, to Leeds City Art Gallery.
Ex: Tate Gallery, *Cotman,* 1922 (224); Manchester 1968 (142).
Lit: S. C. Kaines Smith, *Cotman,* 1926, pp 142, 164, repr fp 142; S. D. Kitson, *The Life of John Sell Cotman,* 1937, p 41, repr No 10.

The sketch shows a horse-gin, many examples of which could be seen in the Coalbrookdale Coalfield. Similar in subject and style to the drawing by Thomas Hearne (item 77).

74. *Coalbrook Dale*
Pencil, 6½ × 11 in (161 × 281 mm).
Inscribed, blc '1802'; brc 'Coalbrook Dale 1802'.
Col: bequeathed by Sydney D. Kitson to Leeds City Art Gallery, 1938.
Lit: as 73.

Possibly shows a mine entrance below a group of houses.

74

75

75. *Coal shaft at Coalbrook*
Pencil, 5 × 9½ in (126 × 240 mm).
Col: P & D Colnaghi & Co Ltd 1973.

Similar to item 74.

76. VINCENT BROOK after John Sell Cotman (1782–1842)
Salt house, Madeley Dale
Lithograph, 9⅛ × 12⅝ in (232 × 322 mm).
Inscribed, blc 'Cotman'; below, 'Salt House Madeley Dale.'; brc 'Vincent Brook, Lith. London'.
Col: V & A (E5213/1919/p. 4).

Presumably Cotman sketched this salt house at the same time as his other illustrations of the Gorge and one must assume that it depicts the hamlet of Salthouses which used to be situated at the downstream end of Jackfield.
See B. Trinder, *Extraordinary District*, p 53, for a description of the Madeley Salt Works by Robert Townson in 1799.

76

77. THOMAS HEARNE (1744–1817)
Coalbrookdale
Pencil, 7½ × 8½ in (191 × 217 mm).
Col: C. Fry, purchased Mellon Collection 1972.

The sketch shows a horse-gin with figures and a horse and cart. Hearne started life as an engraver to Lord Lavington and then worked in London from 1777 producing *The Antiquities of Britain*. He was a member of the Society of Artists and of the Royal Academy.

77

78a

78.   FRANCIS NICHOLSON (1753–1844)

a)   *Near Shifnal*
Lithograph, 8 × 15¾ in (300 × 400 mm).
Inscribed, brc 'near Shifnal', and blc 'F N 1821'.
From *Lithographic Impressions of Sketches from
Nature 1821* by Francis Nicholson. Also occurs
with the inscription, 'Explosion and Fire at
Shiffnal', from *Six Lithographic Impressions of
Sketches from Nature*, 1820.
Col: Salop County Library.
Lit: Klingender 1968, p 183.

b)   *Near Wellington* (not illustrated)
Colour lithograph, 8 × 15¾ in (300 × 400 mm).
Inscribed bc 'Near Wellington, Shropshire';
blc 'F N 1821'; brc 'Printed by C. Hullmandel'.
Col: Ironbridge Gorge Museum Trust.

Nicholson was born at Pickering, Yorkshire;
he executed views of Scarborough and painted
portraits, landscapes and animal subjects. He
settled in London and became President of the
Old Water Colour Society, exhibiting at the RA
between 1789 and 1804. Towards the end of his
life he produced many lithographs. No evidence for an explosion can be seen in the
lithographs, which probably show the ironworks at Snedshill.

79–83.   J. HOMES SMITH (1797–1868)
79.   *The Ironbridge*
Watercolour, 8½ × 11½ in (216 × 292 mm).
Inscribed, below image 'The Ironbridge,
Shropshire, "This bridge was cast at Colbrook
and erected in 1779". Inscription on bridge.';
signed blc 'Homes Smith 1829'.
Col: Shropshire Archaeological Society,
Homes Smith collection, Salop County
Library.

The artist was the eldest son of Edward Smith
and Anne Medlicott of Worcester. The 1841
census returns show a John Smith, artist aged
between 40 and 44 with a son of the same name
aged 14, described as a china painter.

80.   *The Resolution Steam Engine*
Watercolour, 6 × 8½ in (152 × 216 mm).
Inscribed 'Engine House, Coalbrookdale';
signed 'Homes Smith, 1821'.
Col: Shropshire Archaeological Society,
Homes Smith collection, Salop County
Library.
Lit: B. Trinder, *Extraordinary District*, p 90.

81.   *Broseley Furnace*
Watercolour, 5 × 6½ in (127 × 165 mm).
Inscribed, blc 'Homes Smith July 21 1821'; on
mount 'Old Furnace, Broseley'.
Col: Shropshire Archaeological Society,
Homes Smith collection, Salop County
Library.
Lit: B. Trinder, *Extraordinary District*, p 84.

82.   *Coalport Bridge*
Watercolour, 6⅞ × 9¼ in (173 × 233 mm).
Inscribed, blc 'Homes Smith 1828'.
Col: Shropshire Archaeological Society,
Homes Smith collection, Salop County
Library.

83.   *Coalport Rock House and Waterwheel*
Watercolour, 7¼ × 11½ in (184 × 292 mm).
Inscribed below image 'Coalport Rock House
and Waterwheel 1825'; signed 'Homes Smith
1825'.
Col: Shropshire Archaeological Society,
Homes Smith collection, Salop County
Library.

79   80

81   82

83

84

85

86

84–8. ARTHUR HOWE HOLDSWORTH (1780–1860)

84. *Iron Bridge, Colebrook Dale*
Pen, ink and wash, $8\frac{3}{4} \times 5\frac{1}{2}$ in (220 × 140 mm).
Inscribed, blc 'Iron Bridge Colebrook Dale'.
Col: Ironbridge Gorge Museum Trust.

This sketch, made from a point on the north bank of the river looking towards Benthall Edge, must have been executed between 1802 and 1820 as it shows the bridge with timber side arches. In the foreground are several trows, one with its mast lowered.

Holdsworth was a member of Parliament for Dartmouth from 1802 and also held the position of Governor of Dartmouth.

85. *Colebrook Dale at night from the Iron Bridge*
Pen, ink and wash, $5\frac{1}{2} \times 8\frac{3}{4}$ in (140 × 220 mm).
Inscribed, bc 'Colebrook Dale at Night from the / Iron Bridge'.
Col: Ironbridge Gorge Museum Trust.

A sketch so similar in detail to that of the more famous painting by de Loutherbourg that one must assume that either the Severn Gorge really did look like this in the early nineteenth century or that Holdsworth was copying de Loutherbourg's work.

86. *Colebrook Dale from the inclined plane*
Pen, ink and wash, $5\frac{1}{2} \times 8\frac{3}{4}$ in (140 × 220 mm).
Inscribed, brc 'Colebrook Dale from the Inclined Plane'.
Col: Ironbridge Gorge Museum Trust.

From the vantage point of the Hay Inclined Plane, Holdsworth made this sketch which obviously bears great similarities to the Farington (35). On the north bank of the Severn can be seen the smoke of Bedlam Furnaces and the various mine headgears and pumping engines situated in the Lloyds. It is noticeable how many buildings had been erected in Jackfield and Salthouses, and the activity around the Calcutts ironworks is obvious. Two trows are sailing upstream and the whole scene is observed by a rather large lady in the foreground!

87. *From the Iron Bridge at night, Colebrook Dale*
Pen, ink and wash, $7 \times 4\frac{1}{2}$ in (179×115 mm).
Inscribed, bottom margin 'From the Iron Bridge at night Colebrook Dale'.
Col: Ironbridge Gorge Museum Trust.

An unusual view of the Iron Bridge looking from the Tontine Hotel, looking over the bridge towards Benthall Edge with the great wheel on the left-hand side. The road running up Benthall Edge leads to the Benthall iron works. The house now known as Bridge House in the foreground of the picture has a hanging sign indicating that the premises might at one time have been licensed.

88. *Buildwas Bridge*
Pen, ink and wash, $5\frac{1}{2} \times 9$ in (140×229 mm).
Inscribed, brc 'Buildwas Bridge / Colebrook Dale'.
Col: Ironbridge Gorge Museum Trust.

An upstream view of this interesting bridge constructed by Thomas Telford in 1795–6.
The iron work was supplied by the Coalbrookdale Company, which suffered a substantial loss on the contract owing to the failure of the masonry contractor. Compare this sketch with the engineering drawing (43).

87

88

89

90

91

92

89. W. SMITH (active 1810)
Iron Bridge, Coalbrook Dale
Lithograph, $3\frac{1}{4} \times 6$ in (82×152 mm).
Inscribed, bc 'IRON BRIDGE Coalbrook Dale';
below 'Published by W. Smith, July 1, 1810'.
Col: Salop County Library.
Lit: B. Trinder, *The Industrial Revolution*, p 16;
B. Trinder, *Extraordinary District*, p 89.

An upstream view showing the bridge with
timber side arches and the ill-fated stables of the
Tontine Hotel (see item 68).

90–2. Anonymous
90. *Iron Bridge at Coalbrook Dale*
Pencil, $7\frac{1}{8} \times 9\frac{5}{8}$ in (186×245 mm), inscribed,
blc 'Iron Bridge'.
Col: National Library of Wales, vol 90, p. 38.

A downstream view from the north bank,
showing the timber side arches and Benthall
Edge in the background.

91. *River Severn*
Pencil, $6\frac{3}{8} \times 9\frac{5}{8}$ in (163×245 mm), trc 'Coal-
brook Dale'.
Col: National Library of Wales, vol 90, p 37.

An upstream view from the Iron Bridge
showing the development of The Wharfage on
the north bank and Benthall Edge on the left.

92. *Coalbrookdale great wheel*
Pencil, $7\frac{1}{4} \times 9\frac{5}{8}$ in (183×245 mm).
Col: National Library of Wales, vol 90, p 39.

Benthall Big Wheel was a popular subject with
artists; this view, looking across the Gorge,
shows the Hay Farm on the horizon.

93. JOHN GEORGE WOOD, FSA (d. 1838)
A mill at Colebrook Dale
Print, $8\frac{3}{8} \times 12\frac{1}{2}$ in (212 mm $\times 318$ mm).
Title in bottom margin 'A Mill at Colebrook
Dale'; above title 'London, Published by Jno.
Geo. Wood 1814'; trc 'pl 10'.
Col: Ironbridge Gorge Museum Trust.

A plate from *The Principles and practice of
sketching landscape scenery from Nature* (1813).
Wood was a lecturer on perspective at the
Royal Institution in 1807, 1808 and 1809. This
sketch depicts Benthall Big Wheel; note the
variation in the number of spokes in the wheel
from the previous sketch. The corn mill which
was operated by the wheel was built in the late
18th century.

93

94

94. Anonymous
Scene in Colebrook Dale
Lithograph, $4\frac{1}{2} \times 7\frac{1}{4}$ in (114×184 mm).
Inscribed bc 'Scene in Colebrook Dale'.
Col: Mrs Thistlethwaite, Ironbridge Gorge
Museum Trust.

In this lithograph, the bridge almost appears to
be solid, but the side arches are obviously of
timber.

95, 96. JOSEPH POWELL (c 1780–c 1835)
Very little is known about Powell. He was
taught by B. T. Pouncy and from 1796 to 1833 he
exhibited regularly at the RA. He was entered
in the Dictionary of Artists as John Powell, and
it was not until 1948 that his real identity was
established and a number of watercolours were
re-ascribed to him. He is thought to have been
from Bridgnorth, but the only evidence for this
is his intimate knowledge of the area, and the
large extent of his work done there. He toured
widely but kept returning to the Bridgnorth
area. He was the first President of the New
Watercolour Society and he last exhibited there
in the year that he probably died. These
sketches were done between 1816 and 1818.

95. *Sketchbook with 27 drawings of Bridgnorth and
surrounding country*
Pencil, with sepia wash, cover size $7\frac{1}{4} \times 11\frac{1}{4}$ in
(184×286 mm).
Signed, inside front cover 'J. Powell'; inscribed
'*Salop* / Bridgnorth'.
Col: acquired by the V & A (E1857–1946), the
work having been in the possession of C. F.
Powell, the artist's son.
Lit: J. Mayne, 'Joseph Powell', in *Burlington
Magazine*, XC (Sept 1948), pp 267–8.
Ex: Manchester 1968 (231).

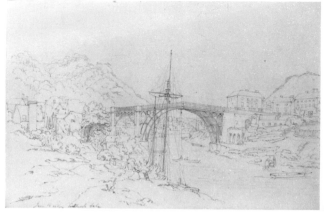

95a

a) *Iron Bridge, Coalbrook Dale*
Inscribed, blc 'Iron Bridge at Coalbrook Dale'.
This sketch, from the same viewpoint as Munn
(item 68) shows the bridge with timber side
arches (ie before 1821) and with the Tontine
stables burnt down (after 1816).

b) *Tykes Nest, Broseley*
Inscribed, blc 'Tykes Nest, Broseley'.
A view of one of the inclines running down
from the quarries on Benthall Edge.

95b

c) *In Coalbrook Dale*
Inscribed, blc 'In Coalbrook Dale'.
Shows Boring Mill Pool, Rose Cottages and a
plateway waggon.

d) *Benthall Lime Kilns*
Inscribed, blc 'Benthall Lime Kilns'.
A view from the top of Lincoln Hill across to
Benthall Edge.

95c

e) *Coalport wheel and pot works*
Shows the water wheel at Swinney Cliff with
associated kiln and, in the distance, the
warehouses and shipping at Coalport. The corn
mill was built about 1805. By about 1820 the
site was occupied by Rock House.

f) *The Wood Bridge, Coalport*
Inscribed, brc 'The Woodbridge Coalport'.
An upstream view of this bridge showing the
cast-iron arches but, since the handrails are of
timber, the sketch must have been done before
their replacement in cast iron in 1818. Alongside the bridge is the tollhouse and large
warehouse. Several trows are seen.

95d

95e

95f

96. *At Sunny Side, Coalbrookdale*
Pencil, 4 × 3 in (102 × 76 mm).
Inscribed, blc 'At Sunny Side, Coalbrook dale 6'.
Col: Morley Tonkin (47), Ironbridge Gorge Museum Trust.
This sketch was p 6 of the Wenlock Sketchbook, the pages of which are now dispersed.

This view depicts the cast-iron bridge over the Upper Furnace Pool which connected Darby Road with Greenbank Farm.

97. Anonymous
Coalport wheel and pot works
Pen drawing, 7 × 12 in (178 × 305 mm).
Col: Morley Tonkin (48), Ironbridge Gorge Museum Trust.

A view of the water wheel and kiln at Swinney Cliff from approximately the same viewpoint as item 95e. Unfortunately the artist is not known, but the drawing probably dates from *c* 1815.

97

96

98

99

98. Anonymous
View from the Severn Warehouse
Pen, ink and watercolour, $5\frac{5}{8} \times 7\frac{5}{8}$ in (143×187 mm).
Col: Ironbridge Gorge Museum Trust.

This amateur sketch, viewed from the site of the present Severn Warehouse, indicates some of the activity which must have taken place around this busy riverside wharf. In the foreground is a large crane used for loading the Severn trows, an empty one of which is depicted tied up alongside the wharf. The wharf is served by various plateways which are shown on the sketch, together with two waggons, one flat-bedded and the other covered with canvas. The picture was painted after 1820 as the Iron Bridge has two cast-iron side arches and on the horizon can be seen an engine house and a gin-pit. Across the river from the warehouse one can see Bower Yard with a trow under construction and sections of timber set out on the bank. One interesting feature is the presence of a female figure in the bottom left corner, standing outside the Swan Inn and holding a pint of beer in one hand and smoking a pipe.

100

99–102. WILLIAM WESTWOOD
Four views of Coalbrookdale and its vicinity, drawn from nature and on stone by William Westwood, published by William Westwood. Coalbrook Dale 1835
India 10/6, Plain 7/6.
Coloured lithographs, inscribed, blc 'drawn from nature and on stone by William Westwood.'; brc 'Published by Graf and Sorret'.
Col: 99, Clive House Museum, Shrewsbury; 100–2, Ironbridge Gorge Museum Trust.

101

99. *View from Cookson's Hill*, $9\frac{7}{8} \times 13$ in (250×330 mm).

Drawn from the top of the hill that is on the west side of Coalbrookdale, this view looks up the River Severn towards a rather fanciful Buildwas Bridge.

100. *The Iron Bridge near Coalbrookdale*, 8×10 in (203×254 mm)

A downstream view of the bridge from the North bank with Benthall Edge in the background.

101. *Coalbrookdale from the north east*, $9\frac{3}{4} \times 13\frac{1}{4}$ in (248×337 mm).

102

Looking from Jiggers Bank towards the large houses on Darby Road with Sunnyside at the extreme right. The Dale works are at the centre left.

102.   *The upper part of Coalbrook Dale,*
15½ × 17 in (394 × 432 mm)

A view of the small cast-iron bridge over the Upper Furnace Pool with a miniature boat. Compare with the sketch by Powell (item 96).

103

103.   EDWARD PRYCE OWEN (1788–1863)
Near the Iron Bridge, Salop, 1836
Sepia wash, 11¾ × 11¾ in (300 × 300 mm).
Col: Salop County Library Ms 201.

A further illustration of Benthall Big Wheel.

104.   W. BANGHAM
Letterhead with the Iron Bridge
Engraving, 5½ × 8 in (140 × 203 mm).
Inscribed, top left 'Iron Bridge, / Shropshire. Bought of Edward Edwards, funerals furnished / dealer in hats / Linen and Woolen Draper. / Silk Mercer, Haberdasher, Hosier etc.; blc 'W. Bangham, Sc., Birm.'; dated 'Xmas 1841' (in manuscript).
Col: Labouchere Collection, Salop County Record Office (A 743).

105.   Attributed to J. FIDLOR
Ironbridge
Watercolour, 14 × 18½ in (356 × 470 mm).
Col: Clive House Museum, Shrewsbury.

A downstream view of the Bridge from the Benthall side, with trows in the foreground and a coracle. Ironbridge church (built 1837) is shown, as is The Wharfage.

106.   *Ironbridge*
Watercolour, 14 × 21 in (356 × 533 mm).
Col: Ironbridge Gorge Museum Trust.

A downstream view of the Bridge from the opposite side to the previous watercolour, looking along The Wharfage, the chief item of interest being a heavily laden cart ascending Tontine Hill and three men weighing wool.

104

105

107

Drawn by J C Bayliss   Engraved by W Bingham Burm

108

109

107–9. JOHN COX BAYLISS
107. *Ironbridge*
Chromolithograph, $8\frac{1}{4} \times 11\frac{1}{2}$ in (210 × 292 mm).
Col: Morley Tonkin (36), Ironbridge Gorge Museum Trust.

A view of Ironbridge from the Broseley Road, looking upstream to the Bridge. The Severn Warehouse can be seen in the distance and the church is prominent in the top right corner.

110

108. *Coalbrookdale from Paradise Fields*
Engraving $5\frac{1}{2} \times 8\frac{3}{16}$ in (140×208 mm).
Title in bottom margin, 'Coalbrookdale from
Paradise Fields'; inscribed, blc 'Drawn by J. C.
Bayliss', brc 'Engraved by W. Bangham. Birm.'.
Col: Ironbridge Gorge Museum Trust.

This view looking up Coalbrookdale shows the
Upper Furnace Pool in the foreground; it was
used by the Company as their letterhead and
receipt.
These lithographs were produced *c* 1856 but
other than that we have no knowledge of
Bayliss's dates. He was from Priorslee, and his
son became Sir Wyke Bayliss, president of the
Royal Institute of British Architects in 1888.

109. *Coalbrookdale*
Chromolithograph, 10×14 in (254×356 mm).
Inscribed, blc 'Coalbrookdale'; brc 'drawn and
lithographed by J. C. Bayliss'.
Col: Morley Tonkin (13), Ironbridge Gorge
Museum Trust.

From the familiar viewpoint of Jiggers Bank,
Darby Road and Sunnyside are evident, with
Broseley on the far horizon.

110. GEORGE PHOENIX
The Iron Bridge, 1907
Watercolour, $30\frac{1}{2} \times 38\frac{1}{2}$ in (775×978 mm).
Inscribed, brc 'Geo Phoenix'.
Col: Institution of Civil Engineers, purchased
from the artist 1907.

Shows, in the foreground, a canal narrow boat
named *Rose*.

111. VERA LOUISE TEMPLE (1897–1955)
The Iron Bridge
Watercolour, $9\frac{7}{8} \times 12\frac{3}{8}$ in (250×314 mm).
Signed blc 'V. L. Temple 1935'.
Col: Ironbridge Gorge Museum Trust.

Vera Temple was the youngest daughter of
Charles Henry Temple, the chief designer at
Maw's tile works in the late 19th century. The
buildings shown next to the bridge were
demolished in the 1950s.

111

112

112. *Worcester Vase, 1820*
Vase, 9¼ in (235 mm) high, with view of the Iron Bridge in sepia as by J. Baker (item 51); hand-painted mark on base, 'Iron Bridge, Coalbrook-dale'.
Col: Ironbridge Gorge Museum Trust.

113. *Iron Bridge Snuffbox, c 1790*
Snuffbox, Birmingham enamel, 1¾ × 1¼ × 1 in (45 × 32 × 25 mm); inscribed, 'A present from the Iron Bridge'.
Col: Private Collection.
Lit: Ian T. Henderson, *Pictorial souvenirs of Britain*, 1974, p 14.

114. *Coalport Mug, c 1825*
Mug, 2¾ in (70 mm) high, with hand-painted view of Bridge in full colour; hand-painted mark on base, 'Iron Bridge, Coalbrook-dale'.
Col: Elton Collection, Ironbridge Gorge Museum Trust.

The painting shows the bridge with iron side arches, and to the right of the bridge is the stable block for the Tontine Hotel.

115. *Coalport Jug*
Jug, 4¾ in (120 mm) high, with hand-painted scene in full colour of the Iron Bridge; inscribed, below spout, 'Francis & / Ann Evans / June 12, / 1828.'; not marked.
Col: Private Collection.

An upstream view of the bridge which by now has iron side arches.

116. *Coalport Mug*
Mug, 4¼ in (105 mm) high, with transfer-printed views of Ironbridge and Buildwas Abbey in magenta; inscribed 'IRONBRIDGE, SHROPSHIRE'.
Col: Ironbridge Gorge Museum Trust.

113

114

115

A transfer print of the John Cox Bayliss chromolithograph of *c* 1856 (item 107).
This transfer was used, on several sizes of mug, in black, sepia and magenta, and also on a teapot stand.

116

117. *Coalport Plate* (not illustrated)
Plate 9 in (229 mm) in diameter, inscribed 'IRONBRIDGE SHROPSHIRE 1826'. View of Ironbridge as item 116. Mark on base 'Made in England' above crown, 'COALPORT / A.D. 1750 WENHAM'; impressed mark, '18K25/2'.
Col: Ironbridge Gorge Museum Trust (Private Collection).

A poor transfer of the engraving by John Cox Bayliss of 1856 (item 107). The date is erroneous and one must assume that the plate was produced in 1926 to commemorate some hypothetical centenary.

118

118. *View of the Severn*, c *1800*
Oil on convex glass, diameter 4¼ in (108 mm), with view of the Severn showing the Iron Bridge and a trow.
Col: Ironbridge Gorge Museum Trust.
One of a pair; the other illustrates the Sunderland Bridge.

119. *Midlander of the Year Award*
Silver, with enamelled centre; overall diameter 12 in (300 mm); enamelled centre 2¾ in (70 mm), with view of the Iron Bridge after Rooker; inscription, bottom centre, 'MIDLANDER OF THE YEAR / 1977 / PRESS RADIO AND TELEVISION AWARD / SPONSORED BY / BASS MITCHELLS & BUTLER / PRESENTED TO / THE IRONBRIDGE GORGE MUSEUM TRUST / AND ITS DIRECTOR NEIL COSSONS.
Col: Ironbridge Gorge Museum Trust.

119

120.   PHILIP WILSON STEER (1860–1942)
Ironbridge
Oil on canvas, 21 × 30 in (533 × 762 mm).
Col: Labouchere Collection, donated to the
Ironbridge Gorge Museum Trust 1978.

121.   JOHN NASH (1893–1977)
Ironbridge, Shropshire
Watercolour and pen and ink, and pencil,
16 × 24 in (406 × 610 mm).
Inscribed 'Ironbridge, Shropshire'; signed
'John Nash 1952'.
Col: S. A. Heneage, Godalming; purchased by
the Ironbridge Gorge Museum Trust 1978.

122.   CLARENCE E. BLACKBURN
The first iron bridge in the world, 1779, at Telford
Pen, ink and watercolour, 32½ × 44½ in
(825 × 1130 mm).
Signed blc 'C E Blackburn'.
Col: Institution of Civil Engineers.
Ex: RA 1976.

Painted before the restoration of the bridge in
1974, this work shows the unlikely presence of
two sailing ships!

123

123, 124. JOHN PIPER (b 1903)
123. *Coalbrookdale*
Watercolour, 16 × 12 in (407 × 305 mm).
Inscribed brc 'John Piper'.
Col: Private Collection.

124. *Ironbridge, 1957*
Crayon, pen and black ink, watercolour and
body colour, 30¼ × 22½ in (769 × 572 mm).
Col: Cecil Higgins Art Gallery, Bedford.

124

Index to Artists, Engravers and Portraits

Numbers refer to illustrations in the Catalogue.

Acknowledgments

Aberdeen Art Gallery	7, 15	Institution of Civil	
Sir Edmund Bacon, Bt	72	Engineers	110, 122
British Library Board	16, 21	Leeds City Art Galleries	73, 74
Trustees of the British		Mellon Collection (Mr &	
Museum	61–4, 66	Mrs Paul Mellon)	23, 49, 77
Cardiff Public Library	52	National Library of Wales	90–2
Clive House Museum,		Royal Institute of British	
Shrewsbury	5, 6, 99, 105	Architects	1
P. & D. Colnaghi & Co Ltd	75	Royal Scottish Museum	11
City of Coventry Art		Salop County Library	24, 78a, 79–83,
Department	14		89, 103
Mrs Judy Egerton	69	Salop County Record Office	55, 104
Sir Alexander Gibb and		Science Museum	12, 45, 60
Partners, Reading	10	Mrs Morley Tonkin	70
Cecil Higgins Art Gallery,		Victoria & Albert Museum	67, 68, 76, 95
Bedford	124		